4002

P9-EMC-680

African Voices

African Voices

AN ANTHOLOGY OF
NATIVE AFRICAN WRITING

Compiled and Edited by
PEGGY RUTHERFOORD

NEW YORK
THE VANGUARD PRESS, INC.

FOREWORD

THIS is us : Africa speaking to Africa and to the world. This anthology is not just about a grumpy, grousing South Africa, but about the whole of Africa : flamboyant West Africa, where men thrust elbows into each other's ribs and laugh broadly over their jokes; East Africa, with its strong Arab influence; traditional Africa, with the funny wisdom that lurks in the antics of animals and the ways of Ju-Ju men and witchdoctors. Here are the dreams about the great things that we yet will do; the long dictionary words and the colourful regalia with which we swathe our dark bodies : that is us.

You can find us in the mealie fields and in the mines; you can find us in the shebeens quaffing 'Macbeth' brews to the jazz and jive of the cities, or outside the grass huts of our fathers, telling tales with the old women. You can see us gaffing each other or breaking suddenly into song and dance; into swear-words, fighting and tears. We are here in the robes of our grandfathers and the tight-trousered dress of the big towns. All this is us.

Here, Africans are creating out of English a language of their own : a language that thinks in actions, using words that dart back and forth on quick-moving feet, virile, earthy, garrulous. Peggy Rutherfoord has delved deep into the literary store of our black Africa to compile this anthology, which shows us in the many moods that are ours. Somewhere or another on the continent there is a new civilization beginning to appear, a new African culture—their are traces of it here.

CAN THEMBA

Drum Publications,
15 Troye Street,
Johannesburg,
South Africa.

PREFACE

I T is becoming increasingly obvious to all thoughtful people that the African continent and the African nations within it are going to play a most decisive part in the immediate future of world history. Indeed, already the importance of Africa is becoming evident.

Yet only those who have had the privilege of living and working in some part of that vast and lovely, yet tumultuous, land know its magic. To the great majority of Europeans, it is still a dark and brooding and mysterious continent. One of the reasons for this is that although there have been in recent years a great number of books *about* Africa, there has been practically nothing from African writers available in English. This anthology, so carefully and comprehensively prepared, will serve to open the door : to give a glimpse of some of the treasure which is there, within. It will also triumphantly give the lie to that idea, so prevalent in some quarters, that Africa is incapable of producing any creative art.

From the Christian standpoint nothing is more valuable to-day than the realization that all Christian missionary endeavours must begin in a humble approach to ways of thought and action differing from our own. Our greatest error in the past has been a far too easy assumption that 'Western' manners, methods and moods were always, *ipso facto,* superior because based upon the Christian ethic. Much of our missionary work has been rendered ineffective by this kind of vicious conceit. Anyhow, to-day, with the vital forces of nationalism stirring from one end of the continent to the other, we cannot afford such complacency. Christianity in Africa is about to meet its sternest challenge. Everything will depend upon the way in which its exponents learn to shed their ideas of racial superiority and gird themselves with the towel of fellowship. I hope that this book—speaking with the authentic voice of Africa—will help us all to a swifter and more complete realization of the richness of culture and the beauty of character which is there.

TREVOR HUDDLESTON, C.R.

CONTENTS

INTRODUCTION

IT is in peace, with the gold dust of time in one's pocket, that one must seek the African on Mount Parnassus. And coming to those evergreen slopes one must tread softly. For the world of African writing is, in some measure, a different world; a world where, outwardly at least, many writers appear to have small desire to see their work in print and literary laurels are of little moment.

And so it is that one does not go boldly as a prospective publisher of their works, but gently, edging round the subject, discussing anything but the real purpose of your visit; talking of the events of the journey: how you have come by dhow from beyond the great coral reef of East Africa, by bicycle up the narrow lanes of Zanzibar, by lake steamer from Ruanda, along the muddy rivers of the Congo; by bus, by train, by Basuto pony.

And then, when the time seems right, the question is put, 'Would you like to suggest something of your writing for the anthology?'

His brow is troubled. 'There are others who write better,' he replies.

You persist.

Then: 'You must ask another about my work. I am no judge.'

At last a writer or a translator will promise to send a manuscript.

The weeks pass, the months disappear, the postman neglects you.

Then word comes: 'I must apologize for the delay, but I have discovered rats in my roof and during repairs all my papers have been moved into positions whence it is impossible to redeem them.'

There are tales in Basutoland. A letter goes forth, like Noah's dove, to seek out the land.

The word returns. A story is on its way. Again one waits, a thread of hope in the hand.

Then: 'I greatly regret to state that I will not be able to accept the offer to contribute to your anthology, because I am occupied with the feudal tenure law suits; secondly because the temporary peripatetic court, of which our area forms the borough, is very far where bridle paths are slippery on rainy days and streams are not bridged.'

And so one must compete with the rains of Basutoland, the rats of Cape Town, to secure the attention of the African writer.

9

Gradually, as the path crosses the foothills of Parnassus and divides into a network of side tracks and cul-de-sacs, it becomes plain that much African writing is hidden away along forgotten valleys, in numerous languages, in remote libraries, or still unpublished in handwritten manuscripts.

Long journeys followed across Africa to meet writers, to visit mission printing presses, to confer with professors and teachers, both black and white. There were months of reading manuscripts, some of them on short loan, which had to be read against time; sometimes throughout snowy London nights, sometimes on the warm deck of a liner homeward bound to Africa once more, sometimes in an aeroplane flying north to the Congo. There were weeks of unearthing from forgotten corners of libraries books printed in limited editions and long out of print; days of nosing through the neat mission bookshops from Mombasa to Cape Town, or along the dusty shelves of the second-hand shops around the British Museum. Hours spent, surrounded by type and printer's ink, perusing the vitriolic articles of the one-man newspapers in Zanzibar. And like the Elephant's Child one asked endless questions, at language schools in London, in Johannesburg, in Cairo; at journal offices in the Congo, at broadcasting stations in Tanganyika.

Even so, after many of those long journeys, after many long hours, I began to see how frequently they ended in blind alleys.

But there were compensations. Such a time was in Mombasa where, wandering at dusk through the streets of the old town seeking the house of a promising writer, I lost my way. A small Arab boy dressed in a long white *galabiya,* like a nightshirt, came to help me in the search. To amuse me from time to time he threw his *galabiya* over his head, danced a little and then winked at me through a large hole in the front of it. And so he skipped and I came after with a bunch of children who had joined us, and we followed him as if he were the Pied Piper, down narrow streets striped by the shadows of tall houses, down streets that had seen the passing grandeur of Sultans, the strange faces of Vasco da Gama and his men; and where now chickens squawked as they escaped from underfoot, where groups of little Indian girls played roulette for toffees on the steps of darkened doorways, past rows of slippers outside a cool mosque, beneath brightly painted balconies, past huge brass-studded Arab doors, and on through courtyards where time seemed to have stopped and the last heat of the day was caught into a fiery trap.

We were lost again.

Then, all at once, from somewhere behind those sightless walls, came the plea of a guitar. My guide beckoned and disappeared through a low doorway. I followed. It was cold and dark inside. I took out my notebook, ready to meet the author. But we did not meet him. Instead we found an old blind African musician sitting on the floor of a narrow room, all shuttered and dark, an Egyptian guitar slung across his knees. The words of his song had been many years on the lips of the tall Swahili people. The blind singer had sung it in the splendour of palaces when, in his younger days, he had been Court Musician to the Sultan of Zanzibar. I leaned against the door, away on a romantic dream, away across the centuries to the silken halls of the mansions of Pate, to lands of minstrels, and maidens at latticed windows. Then a pause, a chuckle, a raucous clearing of the throat. The dream was shattered. A good English sea-shanty, 'Blow the Man Down,' filled the air in broken English. The mansions and the minstrels had gone. I was left with no promising author, no new manuscript in my hand, but left only with a glimpse of buxom wenches and maypoles and good red beef !

But there were times when, unsought, the reward came, as it did once in the most unlikely of places—a London hospital. It was there, when lying in bed, my thoughts far from Africa, that a nurse brought me a pile of manuscripts from a West African writer who was a fellow patient. Soon the search was on once more and I found myself with this huge, bearded West African, who seemed to be rehearsing for a first night of 'Othello,' as he strode up and down, talking of Africa, of writing, of acting. It was a strange meeting, surrounded by the unimaginative smells of a hospital, with a vision beyond the snow and pale sunlight outside, of his home far away in Sierra Leone.

Then there is the struggle against the African sun, which must surely be the greatest ally of procrastination. In lands of the sun, one feels that clocks could be dispensed with, for so often the inclination is to rest when the heat of the sun has slipped into the head and fuddled the brain, and work another day. And the sun of Africa is assuredly on the side of him who sleeps. It is, therefore, with a different conception of time that one must work.

So it is that in this leisure of African time the habit of story-telling still survives. When the sun has gone and the fire is lit at evening, when the oxen rest or the nets are put out to dry ; far away on the high mountains of Ethiopia ; over a glass of palm wine by the great sea that washes the Ivory Coast ; on the street corners of slums and shanty towns, in the old Malay quarter of Cape Town, tales are told ; tales handed down from grandmother to granddaughter, from father to son. On the peaceful coast of Mozambique, beyond the fringe of the village, across a valley to the hilltop *kraals* of Swaziland, one may hear until late into the night the sounds of laughter, of chatter, of song, of storytelling, and coming closer one may see the dark groups enclosing the fires; the children, their eyes bright with the firelight, listening to the tales of old.

And when the last light has left the mountains of Basutoland, when the cattle are *kraaled* and the young herd boy plays his *lesiba,* the old men sitting at their doorways remember their ancestors and tell of their deeds. Was not their chief, Moshoeshoe, wiser than all chiefs? Did he not bring peace to their country? Then were they great.

The praises of the chiefs and of the ancestors are sung all over Africa, often by special court singers, often by wandering troubadours. There were the songs and epic stories that Herodotus found among the troubadours of North Africa. There are the praise-singers, who hire themselves out to gain favours for their clients by the songs of flattery they sing to the music of their *koras.*

These stories, these songs of praise, where have they come from? Against what great canvas and from what stirring of the emotions have they been written?

On the dhows they have come for more than two thousand years, borne on the back of the north-east monsoon, with the spices and bright carpets from Persia, from India and far Arabia. On the lips of the sailors, half Arab, half African, have they come. When the wind is quiet in the sails they have been told; when there is peace on the deck with a space of time to rest, have they been heard. Thus have they come to Mogadishu, to Lamu, to Mombasa, to Zanzibar. From Sofala, said to be ancient Ophir, they have gone inland from the shores of Mozambique along the gold routes of old; across the great kingdom of Monomotapa to Zimbabwe, perhaps, that strange grey city of the past, of history only guessed at. By caravan across the sands of the Sahara they have travelled to the old walled town of Kano. Up and down the dark rivers of West Africa have they passed on the lips of the fishermen, to be told in the ports of the coast. There a tale is told and echoed right across the African continent. Slaves! The word cuts deep into the memory. Freetown, Kilwa, Bagamoyo, Zanzibar!

And what of the Zulu, exiled from the green hills of Zululand? When he lines up at the Pass Offices of Johannesburg to be given permission to share the streets of that city, does he remember the strength of his ancestors? The song the Zulus sing about the pass laws, which ends with the cry, 'We mourn for our country,' tells of their sadness.

It is little more than a hundred years since Chaka and the other great warrior kings of Southern Africa looked at their fair country and dreamed of the great empire they were to build. And what now do they see? Everywhere the seal of their future confronts them; on benches, over doorways to stations and cinemas and public buildings, are seen the well-known words, 'Europeans Only'; so well-known, so common a sight, that they are already absorbed into the very life of the country and few stop to wonder, 'what does this legend mean to the African?' The answer is here in this writing. We have only to read Richard Rives's story, *The Bench*, to know how these words wound.

The tales of Africa have travelled far. Some have been adopted so completely that one forgets, for instance, that the stories of Uncle Remus are not of American origin, but in fact had their beginnings in Africa. And though speculative, it is strange to reflect that the fables of Æsop, told beside the cradles of Europe for so long, may have come from Africa; for it is thought that Lokman, the fabulist spoken of in the Koran, was the originator of these fables: he was described as an 'Ethiopian'—a Negro—slave, and when his stories eventually travelled to Greece he was known as Aithiops, and this, being mistaken for his name, it may have changed in time to Æsop.

For long the stories of Africa were unwritten, handed down by storytellers. But then, at different times and to different parts of Africa came the missionaries. From Portugal, from France, from England, from Italy, from many lands they came, and gradually the indigenous languages of Africa were written down. One by one mission printing presses were set up. The Bible was translated, dictionaries were compiled, hymns were written, and side by side with the missionaries, Africans worked on the translations. There were great figures like Bishop Edward Steere, who not only translated Swahili literature into English, but often in his own printing press set up the type himself and printed the works he translated. And what a great influence these mission printing presses have had in the development of African writing.

And what of the writers themselves? It is only a few of them who write as a means of livelihood. Like writers in all countries, they live and work variously: many of them are teachers in schools and universities, many work at mission stations, some are preachers, some work in government offices, a few are doctors and lawyers and a few are newspapermen.

There is the writer from Sierra Leone who has the solitude of his rooms in Cambridge in which to write, in circumstances so different from those of the writer I visited in a Johannesburg slum. He shared a small room and had to wait until late at night for the peace in which he could write and study the pile of books—the

Milton, the Blake, the Maupassant—that were squeezed onto his washstand. So different again was the background of the old pastor I found living in a dusty township in the middle of the Orange Free State, whose house was a permanent thoroughfare of those who sought his advice and care. And I wondered how he had been able to find the opportunity to write the books he had already had published. There is again the young writer of Lagos, and another, now dead, who lived in the mountains of Basutoland, who were both dependant on the success of their cattle or their crops to finance their education without which, perhaps, neither of them would have become successful writers.

Many have travelled far from their own country to study and to work abroad. Even so, Africa is for the most part still deep in their veins. Whether they be in Africa or away in a strange land ; whether they be shuttled by the restless tide of American life, wrapped round by the hothouse sophistication of a Paris salon, or dreaming away the gentle summer days on the banks of the Isis, the palm-fringed coast, the wide veld, the throngs of Lagos, of Sophiatown, are never too remote.

The journey to Parnassus has been a long one ; through great forests of poetry and prose, through the dark glowing jungle, among the spirits of the ancestors, past crumbling trees, fretted by the persistent woodpecker of race discord, to find the more mature wood. On the way much has been discarded that would be of little interest to the general reader, though of value, perhaps, to the scholar. There were stories and poems and songs of praise that seemed to lose their rhythm and their power of feeling when taken out of their natural language, and so they, too, were left behind.

Many times when the end seemed to be in sight, the promise of something new, of something even better, perhaps, appeared tantalizingly over the next rise. But there comes a time when a halt must be made and, for a while at least, one must pitch camp and go exploring no more.

P. RUTHERFOORD

1954–1958

Southern Africa

The body perishes, the heart stays young.
The platter wears away with serving food.
No log retains its bark when old,
No lover peaceful while the rival weeps.[1]

[1] This is a famous Zulu poem, sung by the older men and women who have passed their prime. It is said to have been sung even before the time of Chaka.

The Prince of the Combined Headquarters

MASUPHA BERENG

IT was one of the shining mornings when the Prince of the Combined Headquarters left his country to seek a golden flower. From his country of green pastures in the southern black continent alone and secretly went he, in the direction of east. And while in the wilderness thus journeying, he met a grey-headed man who asked him where he was going.

The Prince softly replied and said, 'I'm looking for a golden flower, but I do not know where and when shall I find it.'

The old man smiled and said, 'I've heard about the beauty of such a girl who lives in the forest of the west, but one thing I know and that is that you will never come out from that forest, for her father is a cruel and wicked man.'

The Prince then thanked him and turned westwards. Miles and miles he went; weeks and weeks went by, and whilst he was wandering there he met a man armed with a long fork. He was tall and thin with his feet shoe-less.

The man said to him with a thunderlike voice, 'I know that you desire to be my son-in-law, but that depends upon your credentials.' He then directed him to his chasm and told him that he would find there two ladies, but that he must wait till he came back from his ideal business after the sunset.

Thus the Prince went, and when he came to the chasm, he saw there many skeletons. He approached and knocked gently on the door with his finger; and he heard the words, 'Another skeleton?'

Then the door automatically opened. He stepped in, and saw the two ladies sitting facing each other. The elder one stood on her feet and looked at him. The lady blinked, for the attraction of the Prince blinded her. She thought indeed that the Prince must be made of gold slightly mixed with diamond. The Prince also stood amazed, for the beauty of the lady was more wonderful than anything he had imagined. They both stood silent.

Blairsville Junior High School

Blairsville, Pennsylvania

At last the lady approached and kissed the Prince's right cheek, saying with a wonderful voice, 'I am yours if you'll be mine.'

Then the Prince opened his mouth and said, 'This is a great day for me and you! A day with a lilt in it, a joyous, heart-stirring, the world-stands-still day.'

Then the wondrous lady took the Prince out to her father's stable, saying, 'We must leave at once before the arrival of my flaming father, lest he turns you into a skeleton frame.' She led the snow-like horse, which always remained saddled, out of the stable, and mysteriously they disappeared.

When the flaming father returned he went to the stable, as was his daily custom. And when he saw that the stable was empty his anger was so exceedingly flaming that it caused the stable to be prostrated thunderously. Helter-skelterly he went to the chasm and when he found that only his younger daughter was there, he took his telescope and a jack and went out. Automatically the jack lifted him higher and higher till he was taller than every tree in that forest. He began to use his telescope looking all round, and to the east he saw a violent cloud of dust. He looked closer with his telescope, and saw his snow-like horse speeding away. His anger rooted out some of the trees which were nearby and the jack jacked itself down at once.

Then he saddled his second horse and rode away with his front side facing back, lest the dust might blind him.

When she saw that her flaming father came nearer, the eloping daughter took a magical bottle from the saddle-bag. She threw it behind the horse, and where it burst there arose at once great heaps of snow! Thus the flaming father was compelled to turn back. When he came to his chasm he took two shovels. At that time he remembered his yellow pig-headed horse which was indeed miraculous. Just as the snow-like horse, he was always ready, but with no saddle, for the flaming father stood on his back with one foot. Then, with a tempest-like movement, he rode off. He arrived at the heap of snow within a few minutes. He dismounted and took one shovel, which, due to his anger, was red hot, and the snow melted strangely within a short time.

The fleeing lovers were now in the boundaries of the Prince's country of green pastures when they again saw the rapid approach of the flaming father. So the eloping daughter took out of the saddle-bag the other magical bottle and she threw it behind them. All at once the widest and deepest river ever seen flowed out across the land. Giant rocks rolled therein, and reptiles crawled on the banks of that river.

Forthwith the horse of the flaming father stopped; he dismounted and looked at the river! He saw that that final obstacle was beyond his five senses. He saw that even his pig-headed horse could not jump over it, nor could he make a bridge, for the rolling rocks were so large and fearful and the river excessively wide. He even tried to shout at them, but his voice was triple-covered with the sound of the river. He then named that river, 'Beyond Human Comprehension River.' And thereafter he collapsed and died, and there arose a great tempest.

Now, beyond this widest river the Prince and his golden flower dismounted and reposed; they were tired but hilarious. The Prince brushed the lady's hair with the tips of his fingers and said, 'From now onwards, you will be called Queen Ora and thus will it be when we reach my home.'

'But first,' Queen Ora replied, 'you must leave me here and go home alone, for it is a law-like custom that you should go and tell your parents of this, and then come back to fetch me. Only one thing must you remember: let no one kiss you either on the right cheek nor on the left, for if you do, you will surely forget me.'

The Prince agreed and left on foot. His arrival in the village was glorious; the soldiers in the various guardrooms turned out and presented arms; he marched past them to the Palace. There his grandmother was the first one to place her hands on his shoulders and she kissed him twice on his right cheek. And within a twinkling of an eye, Queen Ora was totally forgotten!

Days and weeks passed and Queen Ora remained alone, feeding on wild fruits. Thus it continued for many years, but the beauty of Queen Ora and the Prince remained amazing. And at last Queen Ora realized that the winter of that year would be the coldest one, and she decided to write a letter to the Prince to remind him of the fact that she was lonely. She wrote the letter and posted it during the night at the post-box near the village.

The Prince received and read the letter and he arose as if from a sleep. And thus it was that he remembered the world-stand-still day and happily he went out to find his Queen.

19

The Death of Noliwe

THOMAS MOFOLO

Translated from the Sotho by F. H. Dutton

🕸

Editor's note : This drama of Chaka, the great Zulu warrior king, tells of
how Chaka, when he flees from his home after his own father has ordered
his assassination, meets Isanusi, the witch-doctor and tempter of Chaka.
Isanusi sends him to Dingiswayo, a neighbouring Chief and successor to
Jobe, and there he becomes betrothed to Noliwe, the Chief's sister. Shortly
afterwards Dingiswayo is killed. From this time Chaka is attended by Ndlebe
and Malunga, the two assistants of Isanusi. Gradually, Isanusi tempts Chaka
further and further with promises of greatness, until he offers to make him
the greatest chief of the whole of the African world. But to achieve this a
sacrifice must be made. This time it is the life of his beloved Noliwe.

THE months for reflection appointed by Isanusi came to an end,
and Chaka's decision was not altered; he stood where he did before.
As we have said already, there was one great obstacle to Chaka's
marriage, namely, to whom should he give the cattle? [1] For it was
obvious that he could not take Noliwe in marriage for nothing, as
if she were a wastrel. All the same, Chaka continued to visit Noliwe
and she became pregnant. And now she longed for Chaka's love,
and always wept if she could not see him.

And Chaka loved Noliwe in return; she was the one person one
could imagine Chaka as loving, if he loved any woman with
sincerity. All that is good, all that is beautiful, all that a true wife
can give her husband, Chaka would have got from Noliwe if from
any one. And although he was bartering her away in this fashion
and was planning to kill her, yet his conscience troubled him, and
gave him no rest, telling him always that he had descended from
the level of a man. But because of the chieftainship he smothered
his conscience and pressed on, bearing death on his shoulders.
The next day Chaka, after he returned from watching his regiments

[1] It is the custom among many African people for the bridegroom to give
to the bride's father a present of cattle before the marriage. Since Noliwe
was the last of her family, there was no one to whom Chaka could give the
bride-price.

drill, found that Isanusi and his attendants were no longer there but had gone to procure medicines from the veld and the bush. He entered Noliwe's hut and found her alone with her servant girl, and at once when he saw her he discovered that she had a beautiful brown colour, her skin was smooth and shining, and her beauty was overpowering. There was a look of tenderness in her sparkling eyes. Her voice, when she spoke to Chaka her beloved, far surpassed in his ears the war songs and praises which he had persuaded himself were so beautiful. The tone of her voice was beautifully pitched, clear yet soft, and full of sincerity, without guile or deceit. But above all, her eyes, which so clearly said, 'I am thine, Chaka, my whole self is thine, in life and in death.' At that moment her beauty made him dumb, so that he could not speak, but stood there powerless. He rubbed his eyes and looked away, and when he looked at Noliwe again he found that her beauty was greater than ever; it was a beauty befitting the woman so dearly loved by *Nkulunkulu* [1] who had been chosen out by him to show to men the perfection of womanhood. In Chaka's mind a whirlwind seemed to spring up, a mighty tempest shook him and the dust flew : then he went. When Isanusi returned he said to him, even before Chaka spoke : 'Thou art a man indeed, Chaka. I saw the confusion of thy thoughts when thou didst look upon Noliwe, but thou holdest to thy manhood like a chief, for a chief should not vary his purposes from day to day.'

As Chaka's day approached Noliwe sickened, for she was pregnant, and she was suffering from her burden, although her pregnancy was not yet so advanced that people would take notice. On the evening before Chaka was to go down to the pool, Chaka went to her, taking with him a long needle of the kind used for sewing grain baskets. He found her sitting alone with only her handmaiden, in order to be quiet, and as he entered the handmaiden went out. There was a fire of wood burning and its flames provided a bright light which lit up the hut.

Chaka approached her; he fondled and kissed her and then asked what ailed her. Noliwe answered 'Chaka, my lord, thy brow frowns and thy voice soundeth strained and sorrowful. What hath vexed thee?' Chaka said that nothing had vexed him except that he had been angered by some scoundrel during the drill of his warriors. They continued thus, speaking together happily and exchanging kisses, when suddenly Chaka pressed his strong hand down upon Noliwe's mouth and pierced her with the needle under the armpit. Then he turned her on her side and raised up the part that had been pierced so that the blood might flow back into the wound. When Noliwe was on the point of death her eyelids fluttered a few times

[1] Zulu god or creator.

21

and she said : 'Chaka, my beloved, thou who art now my father, who art Jobe, who art Dingiswayo, who art . . .' The brief candle of her life went out, and her pure spirit fled and went to Dingiswayo to the place of glory above. When Chaka saw her eyelids flutter he was terrified, he began to tremble, and then he fled. When Noliwe was quite dead, Chaka felt within himself something like a heavy stone falling, falling, till it rested on his heart.

He fled outside, but his eyes were dim and he saw nothing, save only the face of Noliwe on the point of death, when her eyelids had fluttered. His ears were stopped, and he heard nothing save only Noliwe's last cry. When he recovered he found himself with Isanusi in the hut and Isanusi was saying words of praise : 'Now thy name hath been enrolled among the number of our chiefs, even the great and the mighty.'

The poor girl who was with Noliwe when Chaka entered was killed; it was said that she had not spoken when Noliwe was ill, so that Noliwe died and none knew of it. And Ndlebe spread the report that it was she who had bewitched Noliwe. Isanusi had now taken from Noliwe the thing he wanted to take (what it was we do not know), and he prepared it as he alone knew how and the next morning he went with Chaka to the river and Malunga and Ndlebe were there. And when they returned Isanusi made haste to go to his own home.

So died Noliwe, daughter of Jobe, sister of Dingiswayo, and wife of Chaka.

Sotho Boyhood

A. S. LEGODI

Translated from the Northern Sotho by G. H. Franz

I SUPPOSE the boys of to-day who spend their days at school have no clear idea of what went on amongst the boys in those days when the days were spent in the wilds with the domestic animals, with the wild animals and with the birds. When we were herding the flocks we were like the animals of the veld; the flocks were entrusted to the tummied folk,[1] and we were off hunting hares and

[1] Little boys.

mice, and organizing drives on birds. When we passed close to a
watermelon field, we hooked the runners with our feet and dragged
the melons along. If by chance we came upon goats that were not
ours, we promptly milked them dry and curdled the milk. It was
the lordlings that ate while the mass was left licking off what clung
to their fingers. We stole the knives of the men and cut sticks. . . .
That is the wizardry of boys.

Motswasele's Farewell[1]

L. D. RADITLADI

Translated from the Tswana by Professor D. T. Cole
and adapted by Peggy Rutherfoord

Is this my country or is it mere soil
Which I must lick with my tongue?
Is this the seat where I must
Rest when banished from the stool
Of chieftainship, in this my country?
Must I live outlawed like a lone beast of prey,
Far, far, from the homage of my people?
Farewell green fields of my home,
I bow my head to you, terrors of this place.
I bow my head to you, O country of despair.
And you our great enemy, you O death,
Receive me into that vast domain of yours.
The fortunes of earth have shunned and escaped me
But life there perchance will free me from torment.
I beseech you approach me, O death, I desire you!
Open O grave, and receive me, I come!
Release me from this world, O spear, I am weary!

[1] Motswasele II was a chief of the Kwena tribe of what is now the
Bechuanaland Protectorate. Some of his tribe rose against him, and here we
see him shortly before the battle in which he is killed and his forces
defeated.

Under the Blue Gum Trees

DYKE SENTSO

AT first, a deep-rooted suspicion and mistrust and then a fear, ugly and profound. Men went about their daily work with their ears a-cocked, their eyes wide open. A rustle among the leaves, a whisper in the night . . . and men's hearts stopped still with misgiving. An unguarded word here, a misplaced word there and men strove feverishly to interpret them into an intelligible whole. Suspicion sprouted and grew. . . . But nothing happened. The people waited with their breaths held in. Two years, four years . . . ten years. . . . Perhaps the fears were unfounded, the doubts misplaced. The people waited still. Ten years, fifteen . . . thirty . . . all was still. . . . Ha ! . . .

But suddenly the suspicions were redoubled and a fear, stark and naked, throttled the hearts of men. They slept with their hearts in their throats, pistols under their pillows. During the day they practised shooting locusts . . . at night locusts shot them. In the cities they barred and barricaded their doors and windows . . . in the farms they hedged in their homes with barbed wire and thin meshed wire netting, and allowed huge dogs to saunter arrogantly within their yards. Then men slept better, with pistols for cushions and dogs for guardian angels. . . .

Such was the time when our story begins. . . .

The big white man stripped off his dull-white overall slowly and hung it on the wall, then he dropped himself easily on a couch and composed himself to sleep. But the sleep refused to come. It was Saturday and with his work finished, his mind sought some form of recreation, which, on the farm, he found difficult to find. He turned over on his side and began to think. . . . At this moment, his wife entered with a big cup of coffee and a few slices of heavily buttered bread.

'Ma,' he said, 'let us visit the Jansens.'

'How can we go there, Japie? We were there only last week !'

'O ja,' he said, 'I had forgotten.' He considered the matter and then :

'Let us go to town then.' Japie had no doubt that his wife would agree immediately. She loved town. But he was wrong.

'Is there anything special in town?' she asked. . . . 'Why not wait until next Saturday. Sunday is *Nagmaal*,[1] you know.' Japie was dumbfounded but then he remembered the new frock in the bedroom and he understood. His wife wanted to wear the new frock then . . . it would be most effective. But what could he do to pass the day?

Suddenly he stood up and went into the bedroom. He pulled a drawer, produced a bottle of brandy and poured himself a glassful. The burning liquid flowed pleasantly down his throat. For a few minutes he experienced a pleasant muddling of the brain. But soon his mind cleared and he found himself thinking all over again where to go and what to do. Again he stood up but this time he went outside and stood in the verandah. Away to the east, the sun had left dawn by four hours. In the west, there was nothing unusual.

Japie Genade went aimlessly from room to room, then he went outside only to re-enter the house. When he went outside again, he watched his son chasing butterflies in the garden, with unseeing eyes he saw him trample one flower after another and he was startled as much as the boy when his wife suddenly called out . . . 'Gert, get out of the garden!' Gert looked once at his mother and then vanished round a corner of the house. A smile creased Japie's face. 'Saturday,' he thought. 'Saturday!'

He paced the verandah slowly with his hands behind his back. Just what could he do? The idea came like a flash. He walked briskly into the house.

'Ma,' he said, 'I am going to tell Moiloa to collect the sheep to-morrow for counting,' and before his wife replied, he was already well on his way towards the stable.

A voice suddenly spoke close by, frightening him, and when he turned round Moiloa was standing below him with his hat in the air. 'Good-day, *Morena!*'[2] he was saying.

'Oh, is it you, Moiloa? Where do you come from—among the trees . . . ?'

'No, *Morena* . . . from beyond them . . . from the graves.'

Japie nodded understandingly. 'But you go to your son's grave often, Moiloa. Is that good?'

'It is good, *Baas*.[3] When I have been to his grave I feel well. It is as if he tells me what to do. You see, he was my eldest son. When

[1] Holy Communion service celebrated monthly by the Dutch Reformed Church.
[2] Chief.
[3] Master.

he died I was left alone. My other son is only twelve years. If I should die what will happen to my children?' Genade did not answer this question. Indeed, he did not know how to answer it, so he changed the subject. He told Moiloa about the sheep and then : 'O *ja,* next Saturday I want you to get ready to go with me to Baas Meyer's farm. There will be a great show there. Is that clear?'

'It is clear, *Baas* . . .'

'Well, good-bye.' . . . Genade trotted slowly homewards.

When Moiloa arrived at the village, the men were drinking and talking in a room specially reserved for the purpose. They did not see him come and when he approached, they were talking about white men.

'Genade is a very good man,' one of them was saying. 'I have never worked for any one farmer for more than four years and yet I have been here six! I do not know what will cause me to leave here.'

'Brother,' said Moiloa, 'you must not speak like that. There are many things to cause you to leave here.'

The men sat bolt-upright and looked at each other slyly. 'Like what?' they shouted in chorus. Moiloa filled his pipe deliberately, lit it and smoked in silence for a while. Then he asked abruptly, 'Have you ever been to Baas de Beer's farm?' Every one of them had been there. 'Well, what did you see there?'

They had seen many things. They had seen sheep and cattle and a new house being built and lands filled with sunflowers.

'Did you see the number of ruins there?' The men looked at each other and tried to recollect how many empty huts they had seen but they failed. Moiloa told them. 'Six,' he said. 'Six! They did not leave because they wanted to. De Beer did not chase them away. Something else did . . . a roaring . . . two, three roaring monsters which do in a day what thirty men do in ten days.'

'What are they?' they asked.

'Go and see them for yourselves. They roar continuously during the day, and when night falls they put on their lights and continue to roar. At night they look like so many ghosts in the mealie-lands and do the white farmers love them! You will see what will happen when they come,' he warned.

The men looked at each other again. 'Moiloa is talking in parables,' one said. 'What did you say?' asked another. The first one replied . . . 'Moiloa is talking in parables.'

The mistiness of dawn dissipated slowly and the gates of 'The Orchards' stood open to welcome people to the farmer's show.

In a big open space under a row of trees nestled fifteen brand new tractors, and all kinds of farm implements. There were planters and windmills; ploughs and trailers; milk-separators and diesel-engines, everything from shellers and waterboring machines to windchargers. Mr. Hoarding stood at the entrance and welcomed the first visitors to his show. 'The Orchards' hummed with life.

Moiloa led a few friends from one exhibit to another, and when they had seen everything he led them aside and swept his hands from side to side.

'These, my friends, are wonderful inventions!' he said.

'Ha!' they said, with their hands on their mouths as they expressed amazement.

'But these things are the things I was telling my friends at home about. You see them yourselves. They do a hundred men's work in one day! They are very good, my friends, but some of us will be the sorrier for their presence!' Genade came beaming to Moiloa, then: 'I am going to buy two tractors,' he said.

'How many, *Morena?*'

'Two, Moiloa!'

'*Jo*,' said Moiloa.

'You do not seem to be pleased, Moiloa?'

Moiloa rubbed his face with his hands uneasily. 'I am pleased, *Morena*,' he said.

Back at the house, the little white boy looked east and then looked west. He looked down, scratched his head and then looked up. The Saturday sun shone brightly down at him. He turned his head from side to side and wished he had gone with his father to the show. Anyway, it did not matter much, for soon his father would be back and then they would go to town. Meantime what to do? His eyes rested on the towering leaves of the blue gum trees and an idea shone through his eyes. Yes, he had found a solution to his regular Saturday problem of what to do with twelve hours of no school, no arithmetic and no real work to do. He rushed into the yard and when he came out he was holding a catapult. He ran into the plantation whistling.

The little black boy was already in the plantation. When he saw the little white boy, his face spread in a happy smile of welcome. 'Why are you running, Gert?' he asked in broken Afrikaans. The little white boy placed two fingers on his mouth and jerked his index finger towards the house.

'My mother,' he said, 'she always says I spoil her garden,' and then without further thought on the matter he asked, 'Where are the birds?'

The birds screamed wildly among the branches, their eyes wild with fear. They flew from branch to branch, from tree to tree, but still the pebbles missed them by fractions of an inch. Some hid in their nests, others flew into the air, but not knowing where to go, they landed again on the trees to scamper away panic-stricken again when the pebbles hit against the branches with a thud.

'Gert,' said the little black boy, 'these catapults are no good; they miss too much.'

'*Ja*,' said the white boy, 'they are no good.' He stopped a little and thought a while. Suddenly he began running. Over his shoulder he shouted, 'I am coming!'

In a little while he was back, but the little black boy gaped in surprise.

'It is a gun,' he said, 'where did you get it?'

'Still,' said the white boy, 'it is my father's.' The black boy came nearer to examine the gun and then suddenly he retreated. The white boy laughed. 'You are afraid!' he said. The black boy continued to retreat. The white boy called to him, 'Man, it cannot shoot . . . it has no bullets . . . look!'

There was a shattering report and both boys fell down like broken trees. The white boy rose and looked at his mate. Blood was gushing out through a small hole above the left eye. Gert turned then, and fled with bulging eyes out of the plantation towards his home.

Japie Genade saw his son running out of the plantation from the van which was then coming towards home. He saw his wife, too, rush out of the house and run towards the boy. He pressed the accelerator hard and the van shot forward. He saw his son point to the plantation. Then his wife saw him. She ran towards the van. He shouted from the van, 'What is it?'

'Gert,' she said, 'he has shot a boy.'

'Where?'

'In the plantation.'

Moiloa heard the words from the rear of the van. When the van stopped he was running towards the plantation followed hard by Genade. In the plantation, they stopped suddenly and looked . . . the little black boy was lying as he had fallen. The two men looked at each other . . . no words passed between them . . . then the white man stepped forward and touched the boy. A tear rolled quickly down his cheek . . . Moiloa nodded.

'There is no more life in him,' he said, and he stood there and looked at his master, then he looked at his son and then he just stood there . . . stunned.

There was no voice under the blue gum trees, no breeze when they lowered the little coffin into the grave beside his brother. There were no tears, the tears had dried up. People just stood near the little mound and drooped their heads. Only one person cried . . . Japie Genade !

When the first tractor arrived, Genade drove it himself and was very excited. He showed it to his boys. 'It cost me a lot of money. A lo–t of money,' he said impressively. The men looked at it. It was red as the setting sun and roared like a charging bull. 'The other is not like this,' he said. 'It is as blue as the sky.' The men clustered around the tractor. Then they shook their heads sadly. One asked, 'Do you remember what Moiloa said?'

'I remember, my brother.'

'Well, those monsters have arrived.'

The men shook their heads and went their ways. The following morning early, one neighbour peeped through the window of his house and spoke with a hushed voice. 'Have you heard that the Ditsebe's are going away?'

'I have heard, brother. Moiloa is at it again . . .'

'No,' said the first. 'It is not Moiloa's action . . . this is retrenchment!'

A few hours later two young men walked towards the mealielands. They spoke little, then . . . 'Have you heard that Moiloa is going away?'

'No, why . . . has he quarrelled with Genade?'

'No, they have not quarrelled. Genade said it was very difficult to part with Moiloa but his financial position compelled him to retrench all the old hands.'

'What did Moiloa say?'

'He asked Genade whether his action was not caused by the fear that Moiloa would one day kill him because his son had shot Moiloa's little boy? Genade denied this vehemently.'

'Well, do you know where he is going to?'

'I do not know, my brother.'

The men fell into silence and then they shook their heads sadly. '*Haai*,' they said. Then after a while :

'Perhaps to-morrow it is you.'

'Perhaps to-morrow it is you.'

And beyond the blue gum trees, in the misty greyness of the morn, before two raised mounds of cold earth, an old man spoke softly with the tenderness of the depth of his heart. 'Farewell, my sons !' he said.

When Moiloa reached home, his wife looked at him. The look

29

spoke and he understood. 'Excuse me,' he said, 'but I am an old man now and I love the quiet and the peace.' His face twitched, there was sorrow in his eyes. He spoke softly, 'I hoped too much. I hoped that someone else would move instead of me.' His children looked at him. There was fear and doubt in their eyes.

'Don't look at me like that my children, don't look at me like that. Where is the horse? I must go and look for work once again.' The eldest girl of eight years came running to her father, 'Let me go and look for work, father.' Moiloa smiled and then he sobered, 'I will go, my child!'

'Can you give me work, my *Baas?*'

'I cannot give you work, my man. I am using tractors. Can you drive a tractor? No, but you are old and you cannot drive it. Go to Baas Adams. Perhaps you will get work there . . .'

'Can you give me work, my *Baas?*'

'I cannot give you work, my boy. I have bought another Jeep and I am using Jeeps. Have you been to Baas Viljoen?'

'Can you give me work, my *Baas?*'

'For twenty nice, shiny round shillings. Come, surely that is good pay. Times are hard and I want to buy tractors too!'

'But I got thirty shillings where I worked and it was insufficient.'

'I cannot give you so much. It is too much for me . . . and for you too. Look, you are old and you cannot do what you used to do. Will you work?'

The sun was sinking fast in the west but the sun had sunk in Moiloa's heart. Twenty shillings . . . !

'I must tell my wife and my children first, *Baas,* but twenty shillings is little money.'

'It is not little, my friend. It is a lot of money and there are many people who want work!'

The sun had set when Moiloa reached home. The sun would never rise in Moiloa's heart. A fire was burning low in the house, and when he sat and cupped his chin in his hands the fire burned lower still. There could never be another day. It would always be darkness and night, the one followed by the other. The children sensed the sadness and shifted closer to each other. Moiloa bent his head and brooded. Wood was put into the fire . . . there was smoke and silence, the one worse than the other. Suddenly Moiloa raised his head. His voice was confident, there was hope in his eyes.

'I am going to apply for a stand in the location to-morrow!'

The flames leaped up in the fire. The wood crackled and cracked. The little children giggled and tittered and Moiloa's wife looked at her husband with a song in her heart. Yes . . . the location. That was what she wanted. That was what every farm labourer strove for . . . that was her ambition! She repeated the little word to herself . . . location . . . location . . . this was living!

'Can you give me a stand in the location, *Baas?*'

'A stand in the location? Who are you? Where do you come from?'

'I come from Baas Genade . . . Baas Japie Genade.'

'Oh, yes, I know him . . . why did you leave him? . . . But no, I cannot give you a stand in the location.' He repeated the words 'I cannot give you a stand in the location.' Another white man had entered and had heard. He looked at Moiloa. His heart wept for him.

'Why can't you give him a stand in the location?'

'Why can't I give him a stand?' the first man repeated incredulously . . . 'Why? Because who is going to work on the farms if all these poor people come to the locations? . . . Besides, the locations are full already . . . filled with old idle hands, and they are supposed to be labour reserves for the towns!' The other white man was not satisfied. They argued, they almost wrangled. Then suddenly the one gave in. 'You know,' he said, 'it is unfair . . . it is unsympathetic . . . but,' he said, 'what can I do? It is against the law!'

Moiloa had heard and had understood. There was no hope for him here. No haven for his there. He must go back to the farms and seek a new home. He looked forlornly about. The question hit him hard . . . where? He felt very tired and there was something wrong with his knees. He could scarcely get on the horse.

'Baas Viljoen, will you take me on?'

'Oh, is it you? Let me see. Yes . . . but I have since found out that I cannot pay you twenty shillings. I will give you eighteen shillings. Will you work?'

There was a queer film in the eyes, a queer trembling of the voice, as if it was hard to speak. . . . 'I will work, *Baas!*'

The branches and twigs of the mimosa trees brushed and crackled loudly as a dry branch was broken here and a twig was picked up there. Then suddenly the woman, with a bundle of firewood on her head, stopped short in her tracks, and listened. Before her, a man, with hands held aloft and looking steadfastly above him, was praying . . .

'Please Lord, take me to your land of promise and rest where there is neither want nor care . . . where there is neither sorrow nor night.'

The woman did not wait for the man to finish his prayers. She retraced her steps carefully and when she reached her home she made a fire as if nothing had happened. When her husband came in, he found breakfast ready for him, and as he began to eat in silence, his wife abruptly spoke :

'Moiloa, I want to die !'

He was shocked and for a moment he could not speak. Then . . .

'What did you say?'

'I said I want to die.'

'Why do you want to die?'

'Because I think it is wrong for me to live a life of despair and have no hope for the future . . . it were best that I should die.'

'But how can you die? What about the children and what about me? Do you lack anything . . . are you not satisfied with your lot?'

She did not answer him immediately. Instead she put more fuel into the fire.

'You do not want me to die?'

'I do not want you to die.'

She turned then and looked steadily at her husband. 'What is it?' he asked.

'I am sorry, but this morning you were praying to die. Is that right?' He was ashamed and embarrassed. It was only natural and human that he should attempt to deny it, but when he looked at his wife, true light dawned on him.

'I am sorry, my dear. I did not realize how my prayer would affect you. Please pardon me. . . . I shall work and hope !'

Mr. Japie Genade was very happy . . . doubly happy. It was the happiness of success. He had just parted with his last guest who had congratulated him on his recent election to the Town Council. Mr. and Mrs. Genade sat on the verandah of their new home in town and enjoyed their happiness in silence.

Mrs. Genade thought of her previous home on the farm. She had lived well there. But many times she had been very lonely. When her husband was away, she had suffered from a terrible fear . . . the fear of being alone with many black people around her. Her husband had often reprimanded her for it, but the fear had remained real to her. Her husband had told her that it was imaginary . . . black people were faithful, and when treated well, could always be relied upon. But she read newspapers and in the newspapers were many stories . . . like the ones she had read in her old history book a few years ago at school. . . . They must be true ! On the farm there were jackals too, but she did not fear these. People, too, told strange eerie ghost stories . . . but these did not frighten her . . . her fear was the fear of black people. That was why she had kept her husband's gun . . . the one her son had used in the accident . . . in the corner of the kitchen, behind the dresser. There it was within easy reach in case of an emergency, but the emergency never came, what came instead was tragedy and remorse. . . . She thought of the incident . . . the shiny buttons of the police uniforms . . . the stricken faces of the white and black people . . . their questions :

'Where was your husband?'

'Why was the gun kept within such easy access?'

'Were the boys friends, did they often play together?'

She shook herself free from these thoughts . . . all that was over now . . . she had a lovely house in town and many friends. A policeman passed her house every day on his regular beat . . . this was living!

'Ma,' said Genade, 'that was a neat little deal I made, eh? Twentythousand pounds with surface rights to the farm. . . . Ha! I always thought there was gold on the farm. . . . It brought me in a tidy little sum and I now can think of that little business I always dreamed to build for myself. It will be pleasant to live here.'

His wife did not answer him. She was much too happy for that. She remembered the nice words that people had spoken to her during the day . . . how people looked at her when she walked in the street. She could almost hear them. 'That is Mrs. Genade, you know, the wife of Mr. Genade who sold his farm for twenty thousand pounds!' She had always desired a mink . . . perhaps . . .

A dark old man passed in the street. Genade stared at him. 'Moiloa,' he called . . . 'Moiloa!' The man stopped and looked at them. 'Did you call?' he asked. He came nearer. Genade saw his mistake then. The man was not Moiloa but he looked very much like him. 'I am sorry,' he said, 'but I thought you were a certain servant who once worked for me.' The black man went on his way.

But this incident had spoiled the day for Genade. He wondered how Moiloa was faring. His son, he remembered, had killed . . . he corrected hurriedly, had been the cause of the death of Moiloa's son. He remembered too that it had been found to be accidental shooting at the inquest and that Moiloa had felt the same and had shown no animosity. He remembered vividly Moiloa coming to him after the inquest . . .

'It is all over now,' he had said . . . 'I am very glad . . . one does not always want to talk about a sad thing, but to remember that they were such friends.' Genade remembered these words and he decided.

The following day he found Moiloa hard at work, with the sun beating down on him. The oxen looked at him with anticipation; they thought he had come to release them. No sweat ran down

Moiloa's face. Perhaps he had no more sweat left in him. Moiloa looked at Genade. . . . Could it be him? . . . Yes, it was. Genade had not changed, but the clothes and the car. . . . Genade spoke.

'I have come to fetch you. You know I live in town now, I have sold the farm.' Moiloa was radiant with happiness but he did not lose his balance.

'Where will I live, *Baas*. I cannot live in a little room at the back, you know. . . . I have a family and some animals. Can you get me a stand in the location?'

Genade raised himself up . . . to the height of a rich man. 'I will see about that,' he said.

'It will be difficult,' Moiloa warned.

Genade raised himself to his full height . . . the height of a rich town councillor.

'With me,' he said, 'many things are possible. You know that, don't you?'

Moiloa knew and he knew, too, that with white people, many things were possible . . . were made possible. But that did not matter at the moment. What mattered was that he would get a stand . . . his life's ambition.

'Thank you very much,' he said . . . and then, 'Thank you very much.'

A visitor is not to be regarded as to his face, but as to his stomach.[1]

[1] An Ila proverb from Northern Rhodesia.

Song of Praise to the Creator

Collected by G. H. Franz and S. Kgomedi Lekgothoane

Translated from the Sotho by G. H. Franz

INVOCATION

Perfection ever rising to perfection,
The man who fashioned mountains and rocks!
Purity Immaculate,
Wood white and unblemished.

Guardian of nation upon nation,
Lone creator of firmament and horizon!
Origin of nation upon nation!
Even before birth the King!

The one of there! The one of here!
The one of here! The one of there!
The one of everywhere, above and below!
The knower of all!
The beautiful, knower of the innermost!
Lord of wisdom, above and below!
The depth too deep for the measure stick.

Lord of heaven's vault!
Lord of that which endeth not! Lord of the everlasting!
The rock which has withstood the fire!
Lord of that which endeth not, both the going out and
    the coming back.

That which endeth not is never understood.
King of kings, an unfathomable thought!
I, the mother, even though scandal is spoken,
Yet ever and again we clap hands,
And all slides off my shoulders.

The rock has been fashioned a shining beacon on the
   mountain top.
Thither we flee from raging storms.
Knife carving portions for others,
Yet, the while, carving for the master himself.
Where the front hoof has trod,
There also shall the back hoof tread.

THE PRAISE

I, the revered of all nations,
I, for ever the same,
I, the leader to pastures and guide back to the kraal,
I am the origin of all sustenance,
I am the mother of all nurture,
'Tis I that reign, father of all bounty,
I, the bellow of the bull.
Ye are fed, ye are satisfied.
I, the great elephant, am your mother,
Your mother, see how great my breasts!

I embrace unlimited spaces,
I am not as small as you,
You little urchins dancing round the cooking pot,
Eyes fixed on the dishing up.
I am your foster-mother.
Ye and I are head and cheek,
Never can they be parted.
I am the royal bead on the brow of kings, the beautiful
   raiment.
Master-tutor above and below,
Rock that has withstood all tests.

Keep it Dark!

A traditional drinking song from Southern Rhodesia
translated from the Zezuru by Hugh Tracey

Keep it dark!
>Don't tell your wife,
>For your wife is a log
>That is smouldering surely!
Keep it dark!

Keep it dark!
>Don't tell your wife,
>For your wife is a pot
>That resounds to the breeze.
>And then 'Bang'!
>It's all out and about!
Keep it dark!

Mob Passion

D. C. THEMBA

🐾

Editor's note : 'Mob Passion' is a story told against a background of the 1951–52 riots in Newclare, a township eight miles west of Johannesburg. Fighting broke out between a gang, composed largely of Basutos working on the Rand mines, who called themselves 'Russians,' and the Civil Guards. The Russians had been terrorizing the people of that district, and the Civil Guards were formed of members of other tribes, in order to protect themselves and the people of the township. It was after the Civil Guards had taken the law into their own hands and made reprisals on their enemy, that the strife turned into gang warfare.

THERE was a thick crowd on Platform 2, rushing for the 'All Stations' Randfontein train. Men, women and children were pushing madly to board the train. They were heaving and pressing, elbows in faces, bundles bursting, weak ones kneaded. Even at the opposite side people were balancing precariously to escape being shoved off the platform. Here and there deft fingers were exploring unwary pockets. Somewhere an outraged dignity was shrieking stridently, vilely cursing someone's parentage. Fuller and fuller the carriages became. With a jerk the electric train moved out of the station.

'Whew !' panted Linga Sakwe. He gathered his few parcels upon his lap, pressing his elbows to his side pockets. He did not really have any valuables in these pockets ; only long habit was working instinctively now.

Linga was a tall, slender fellow, more man than boy. He was not particularly handsome ; but he had those tense eyes of the young student who was ever inwardly protesting against some wrong or other. In fact, at the moment he was not a student at all. He was working for a firm of lawyers in Market Street. He hoped to save enough money in a year or two to return to university to complete an arts degree which he had been forced by circumstances to abandon.

People were still heaving about in the train ; but Linga was not annoyed. He knew that by Langlaagte, or perhaps Westbury, most of these folk would be gone and he would be able to breathe again. At Braamfontein many people alighted; but he was not thinking of his discomfort any more. He was thinking of Mapula now. She had promised that she would be in time for this train. That depended, of course, on whether she succeeded to persuade the staff nurse in charge of the ward in which she worked to let her off a few minutes before time.

The train slowed down. Industria. Linga anxiously looked outside. Sure enough, there she was! He gave a wolf-whistle, as if he was admiring some girl he did not know. She hurried to his carriage, stepped in and sat beside him. They did not seem to know each other from Adam. An old man nearby was giving a lively narration in the grimmest terms of the murders committed at Newclare.

At Westbury the atmosphere was tense. Everybody crowded at the windows to see. Everywhere there were white policemen, heavily armed. The situation was 'under control,' but every one knew that in the soul of almost every being in this area raved a seething madness, wild and passionate, with the causes lying deep. No cursory measures can remedy; no superficial explanation can illuminate. These jovial faces that can change into masks of blood-lust and destruction with no warning, on smallest provocation! There is a vicious technique faithfully applied in these riots. Each morning these people quietly rise, and with a businesslike manner hurry to their work. Each evening they return to a Devil's Party, uncontrollably drawn into hideous orgies. Sometimes the violence would subside for weeks or months, and then suddenly would flare up at some unexpected spot, on some unexpected pretext.

At Newclare, too, from the train all seemed quiet. But Linga and Mapula knew the deceptive quiet meant the same even here. The train skimmed on, emptier. Only when they had passed Marais-burg did these two venture to speak to each other. Linga was Xhosa and Mapula Sotho. A Letebele [1] and a Russian! They had to be very careful. Love in its mysterious, often ill-starred ways had flung them together.

Linga spoke first.

'Sure you saw no one who might know you?' he asked softly.

'*Eh—eh,*' she replied.

She fidgeted uneasily with the strap of her handbag. His hand went out and closed over her fingers. They turned simultaneously to look at each other.

---

[1] A contemptuous word applied by all Sotho groups to the Nguni groups (Zulu, Xhosa, Swazi, etc.). Originally the term referred to the followers of Mzilikazi who broke away from Chaka and who later harassed the Sothos. The plural of Letebele is Matabele.

A sympathetic understanding came into Linga's eyes. He smiled. 'Rather tense, isn't it?' he said.

She looked past him through the window.

'Witpoortje!' she exclaimed. 'Come, let's go.'

They rose and went to the door. The train stopped and they went out. Together they walked to a bridge, went over the line and out by a little gate. For some two hundred yards they walked over flat stubbly ground. Then they went down a mountain-cleft at the bottom of which ran a streamlet. They found a shady spot and sat down on the green grass. Then suddenly they fled into each other's arms like frightened children. The time-old ritual, ancient almost as the hills, always novel as the ever-changing skies; long they clung to each other, long and silent. Only the little stream gurgled its nonsense; these two daring hearts were lost in each other. The world, too—good, bad or indifferent—was forgotten in the glorious flux of their souls meeting and mingling.

At last Mapula spoke—half cried:

'Oh Linga! I'm afraid.'

'Here where the world is quiet?' he quoted, with infinite softness. 'No, dear, nothing can reach and harm us here.' Then with a sigh: 'Still, the cruellest thing they do is to drive two young people like guilty things to sneak off only to see each other. What is wrong with our people, Mapula?'

She did not answer. He lay musing for a long time. She could see that he was slowly getting angry. Sometimes she wished she could understand the strange indignations of his spirit and the great arguments by which he explained life. Most times she only yearned for his love.

'They do not see! They do not see!' he continued vehemently. 'They butcher one another, and they seem to like it. Where there should be brotherhood and love, there are bitter animosities. Where there should be co-operation in common adversity, there are barriers of hostility, steeling a brother's heart against a brother's misery. Sometimes, 'Pule, I understand it. We have had so many dishonest leaders, and we have so often had our true leaders left in the lurch by weak-kneed colleagues and lukewarm followers that no one wishes to stick his neck out too far. Where is the courage to weld these suicidal factions into a nation? The trouble is, very few of us have a vision comprehensive enough of our destiny! I believe God has a few of us to whom He whispers in the ear! Our true history is before us, for we yet have to build, to create, to achieve. Our very oppression is the flower of opportunity. If not for History's Grand Finale, why, then, does God hold us back? Hell! and here we are, feuding in God's dressing-room even before the curtain rises. Oh!— ' He covered his face and fell into her lap, unable to say any more.

Instinctively, Mapula fingered his hair. 'In God's dressing-room,' she thought. 'What does it mean?' But his anguish stabbed at her heart. Trying to forget herself, she only sought within her a tenderness to quell the bitter wretchedness she had heard in his voice.

'Linga, no! Let me show you something else—something that I understand. It is no more so long before you and I can marry. I dream about the home that we are going to have. I . . . I want that home, Linga. You taught me that woman's greatest contribution to civilization so far has been to furnish homes where great men and great ideas have developed. Moreover, there's our problem. Let us rather think of ways of handling my father. No, no; not now. Let us think now of now.'

Thabo was running faster now that he was nearing home. His mind was in a whirl; but he knew that he had to tell his father. The lop-sided gate was in the far corner, so he smartly leaped over the fence where it was slack. He stopped abruptly at the door. He always did when there were people. But now, he soon realized, these people were his two uncles—Uncle Alpheus and Uncle Frans. He knew how great news always brings a glory of prestige on the head of the bringer. Thabo felt himself almost a hero now; for these two men were die-hard stalwarts in the Russian cause. Uncle Alpheus was a romantic firebrand. Uncle Frans was a scheming character of the power-behind-the-throne variety. They were complementary to each other: together, a formidable team.

'Father, where is he?' hissed Thabo, breathing hard. The excitement in his voice aroused every one.

'Holy Shepherd! What's the matter, boy?' cried Uncle Alpheus.

'Mapula, Mapula. She loves with a Letebele.'

'What!' exploded Uncle Alpheus. 'Where is she?' Then more calmly: 'Come'n, boy. Tell us everything more quietly; your father is out there?'

'J-J-Jonas t-t-tells me—J-Jonas is a boy who works with me— Jonas tells me that Mapula loves with a Letebele. They always meet at the hospital; but never in the sitting-room. He hopes to marry her.'

'Never!' barked Alpheus. Just then the door burst open. A party of men carried in the limp form of Thabo's father. He was unconscious, and blood streamed all over his face. Beyond them, just outside the door, a crowd had gathered. Everyone was at once asking what had happened. As the news spread, ugly moods swept the crowd. Ra-Thabo was carried into the bedroom and tended by

41

the women. Alpheus and Frans returned to the fore-room and conferred.

'What now?' Alpheus asked Frans.

'Of course, we must revenge. You will talk to the people—the women. Talk fire into them. Connect it with the Mapula business; that'll warm them. Suggest drugs—a Letebele must use drugs, mustn't he? I'll be in the house. Just when they begin to get excited I'll arrange to carry Ra-Thabo out—to the hospital, you know. See if we can't get them bad!' he smiled cheerlessly.

Outside, the crowd—mostly women—was thickening. Even in the streets they could be seen coming along in groups, blanketed men and women. From the house Thabo and his little sister, Martha, joined the crowd. It was obvious that their uncles were going to do something about it.

Alpheus stepped on to the little mud wall. He raised his left hand and the blanket over it rose with it. That movement was most dramatic. In a few moments the crowd moved closer to him and became silent. Then he began to speak. He began in a matter-of-fact voice, giving the bare fact that Ra-Thabo, their leader, had been hurt. Warming gradually, he discussed the virtues of this man. Then he went on to tell of how this man had actually been hurt. Not confused fighting nor cowardly brutalities rose in the mind as this man spoke, but a glorious picture of crusaders charging on in a holy cause behind their lion-hearted leader. Oh, what a clash was there! The Matabele were pushed beyond Westbury station. There the heroes met a rested, reinforced enemy. For a moment all that could be seen was the head of Ra-Thabo going down among them. The clang of battle could be heard; the furious charge could be seen, in the words of this man who was not there. The Basutos fought desperately and won so much ground that their all but lost leader could be rescued and carried back home. And what finds he there? Alpheus's voice went down, softer and heavier, touching strings of pathos, rousing tragic emotions which the hearts present had never before experienced. There was an automatic movement in the crowd as everybody strained forward to hear. In awful, horror-filled whispers he told of Ra-Thabo's daughter giving herself to a Letebele. 'The thing is not possible!' he hissed. 'It would not have happened if the maid had not been bewitched with drugs. Are you going to brook it!' he cracked. 'No!' all the throats roared. 'Are you ready for vengeance!' 'Now!' thundered the mob. Someone in the crowd shouted '*Mule!*' [1] Then the women took up their famous war-cry, chilling to a stranger, but driving the last doubting spirit there to frenzy and fury.

[1] Sotho for 'hit' or 'strike.'

Ee! — le! — le! — le! — le! — le! — le! — Eu! Eu! Eu!

Now they were prancing and swaying in uninterpretable rhythms. A possessed bard in their midst was chattering the praises of the dead, the living, and the unborn; his words clattering like the drumsticks of a fiend.

'Let us go past Maraisburg and attack them from the rear!' yelled Alpheus over the din.

At that moment the door of the house went open. The mob which had been on the point of dashing out recoiled. The sight they saw stunned them. Frans and two other men were carrying out Ra-Thabo, besmeared with blood. Thabo saw Uncle Alpheus leaping with trailing blanket and yelling, 'To Maraisburg!' Again he leaped over the fence into the street. The mob followed hard on his heels.

As the last blanket swept round the corner, Frans turned back to the injured man. His two helpers had also been drawn in by the irresistible suction of mob-feeling. With a smile, he said to the unhearing Ra-Thabo: 'I'll have to get a taxi to take you to hospital, brother.' Then he carried him back into the house.

Late in the afternoon the train from Randfontein suddenly stopped at Maraisburg. Everybody was surprised. Something must be wrong. This train never stops at Maraisburg. Then suddenly!

'All Change! All Change!' And more brusquely: 'Come'n, *puma! Puma!*' [1]

Linga and Mapula hurried out. News had arrived that trouble had started again at Newclare; more seriously than usual. All trains from Randfontein were being stopped here and sent back.

Shrugging his shoulders, Linga drew Mapula away, and arm-in-arm they strolled along the platform, out by the little gate, into some suburban area. For a time they walked on in silence. Then Mapula spoke.

'I hope I'll get back in time,' she said.

'Let's walk faster, then. We might get a lift outside the suburb.' They walked into the open country. Linga knew that if he could only find a certain golf-course somewhere around here, he would know where the road was. Meanwhile, they had to stumble on over rough country, and Mapula's cork-heel shoes were tormenting her toes. She limped on as stoically as she could. Linga did not notice her suffering as he was looking out for familiar landmarks. Those trees looked suspiciously like the golf-course to him.

When they reached the trees Mapula said: 'Linga, let us rest here; my toes are suffering.'

'All right,' he replied. 'But I must look for the road. Let's look

[1] Zulu for 'get out.'

43

for a cool place where you may rest, while I search for the golf-course.'

'Mm.'

He led her amongst the trees. She sat down and pulled off her shoes. When he thought he saw a shadow of distress flit across her brow, he bent down, took her hand, pressed it, and then muttered : 'Back in a moment, sweet.' He rose slowly, looked at her in-decisively, then turned away slowly and walked off.

He did not search far before he noticed a torn and faded flag. The hole was nearby. Suddenly he emerged from the cluster of trees, and came across the road. But his attention was caught by a horde of Russians pursuing a woman who came flying towards Linga. Should he chance it? he wondered. He spoke fluent Sesotho and believed he could pass as a Mosotho, possibly as a Russian. He quickly drew a white handkerchief from his trouser-pocket and tied it round his head. This made him, he knew, an active sup-porter of the Russian cause. Skirts flying, the woman sped past him. Facing the mob, he shouted :

'*Helele!*' [1]

All its wrath spent, the mob crowded round out of sheer curiosity. Some were even in a jocular mood now ; one playing lustily on a concertina. But here and there Linga could see deadly weapons, snatched up in their hasty exodus from Newclare. He spoke to them in fluent Sesotho, taking his idiom from Teya-teyaneng. He asked if that was the road to Newclare ; he said that he worked in Roode-poort, but was going to Newclare because his uncle there wanted more man-power in the house. Won't they please tell him where this road is?

'*Che!* It is no Letebele this ; this is a child of at home,' remarked Alpheus.

'*Kgele!* You speak it, man,' said a burly fellow. Then everyone directed Linga how to get to Newclare.

As Fate would have it, just then Mapula came running, shoes in hand and stockings twisted round her neck.

'Linga ! Linga, darling mine ! What are they doing to you?' she screamed, as she forced her way through the crowd. Linga stiffened. When she came to him she flung her arm around him and clung to him with all her strength, crying all the time. Then she saw her uncle stupefied like the rest of them, standing there. She fled to him and begged him to save her lover. He pushed her aside and walked up to Linga. He stood before him, arms akimbo.

'*Ehe!* So you are a Letebele, after all. You lie so sleekly that I can understand why my niece thinks she loves you.' Then he swung

[1] Sotho for 'hail.'

44

round, his blanket trailing in an arc: 'Friends, we need go no further. This is the dog that bewitched my brother's child. Let's waste no time with him. Tear him to pieces!' The mob rushed upon Linga: *'Mmate! Mmate!'* [1]

'Uncle! Uncle!' cried Mapula. But even as she cried she knew that nothing could be done. She had courted the contempt of her people; and she understood now that all her entreaties were falling upon deaf ears. Whether from convenience or superstition—it did not signify which—she was considered the victim of the Letebele's root-craft.

From the scuffling mob suddenly flew an axe which fell at her feet. In a flash she knew her fate. Love, frustrated beyond bearing, bent her mind to the horrible deed.

Mapula acted. Quickly she picked up the axe whilst the mob was withdrawing from its prey, several of them bespattered with blood. With the axe in her hand, Mapula pressed through them until she reached the inner, sparser group. She saw Alpheus spitting upon Linga's battered body. He turned with a guttural cackle—*He-he-he! He-he-he!*—into the descending axe. It sank into his neck and down he went. She stepped on his chest and pulled out the axe. The blood gushed out all over her face and clothing. That evil-looking countenance she gradually turned to the stunned crowd, half lifting the axe and walking slowly but menacingly towards the largest group. They retreated—a hundred and twenty men and women retreated before this devil-possessed woman with the ghastly appearance. But then she saw the mangled body of the man she loved and her nerve snapped. The axe slipped from her hand and she dropped on Linga's body, crying piteously:

'Jo-o! Jo-o! Jo-na-jo! Jo-na-jo!'

Someone came and lifted her up. Someone else was dragging Alpheus's bleeding corpse by the collar so that his shoes sprang out one after the other.

The crowd was going back now. All the bravado gone, they were quiet and sulky. Only the agonized wailing of Mapula. Every breast was quelled by a sense of something deeply wrong, a sense of outrage. The tumult in every heart, feeling individually now, was a human protest insistently seeking expression, and then that persistent wail of the anguished girl, torturing the innermost core of even the rudest conscience there. The men felt themselves before God; the women heard the denunciations of thwarted love. Within they were all crying bitterly:

'Jo-o! Jo-o! Jo-nana-jo!'

[1] Sotho for 'strike him.'

Umamina

B. W. VILIKAZI

Translated from the Zulu by R. M. Mfeka and
adapted by Peggy Rutherfoord

Come Mamina,
Come let us stretch our legs and thither go,
There where it is wilderness
There where water fountains spring
Dampening the deep green rocks,
Slippery with slimy moss.

Nay Mamina,
Come out as though to draw water,
Carry a calabash and descend to the river.
There you will find me under the water-myrtle
Heavy in full bloom,
Black and oozing with thick juice.

Come Mamina,
Alone, you are bright with crimson hue,
Your path adorned with gaudy colours,
Blossoming with flowers,
Which stoop before you
Bowing their heads on the earth.

Come Mamina,
When you did gaze on me, ebony maiden,
I knew not whither I would go,
My knees quivered, my weapons dropped,
I was filled with the bitterness that lurks in the
    heart
Like a wild beast, and is called love.

Alas, I seek you, Mamina,
You have hidden in the fields of dry grass.
The dry grass is my soul,
Yet you are loitering there,
Gathering blackberries, herbs and creepers.

It is not the national song of shields and knob-
    kerries I sing.
In truth I chant in harmony with the music of
    your reed-pipe,
Whose tunes I hear in the land of Chaka.
I heard and listened and knew.
I beheld your dark complexioned lips
Close over the singing reed-pipe,
Which recalls the golden-rumped canary of the
    forest.
I would that it were blown by the heart
Which harbours thought and feeling.
You have made me grow thus with love,
That I no more appear as a Zulu
Within the courtyard of the black people.

Your love and mine, O Mamina,
Excel the mind, beyond the power of the diviners,
Whose magic bones are strewn on the ground.
They grind herbs and poisonous bushes.
'In truth, are you not deceiving me, Mamina?'
I ask you, as I gaze into
The centre of your eyes without blinking :
'Are you not one of the ancestral spirits?'
Perchance you have lost your way,
On your journey to the gates of Heaven,
And have branched off to Earth
And chanced on the roots of love.

Come Mamina,
You are the star of my soul
You alone are in the depth of my veins
Which make my heart tremble.
You are like the track of the field rat
Which winds through old grass and heads far off.

Come Mamina,
I feel loneliness steal over me.
This earth affords no refuge for me.
Come and lead me to your land, Mamina.
There let us solve the mystery of this love,
That I may know it, Mamina;
Know it wholly with the spirit of the ancestors.

Rammone Returns to the Kalahari

M. O. M. SEBONI

Translated from the Tswana by Professor D. T. Cole and
adapted by Peggy Rutherfoord

&

Editor's note : Rammone, who grew up in the wilds of the Kalahari desert,
left his home to go and work in the gold mines of Johannesburg. That was
his first journey by train and, indeed, the first time he had seen a train and
he had been quite overawed and terrified. Now he is returning to his own
country.

W H E N he saw the multitude of people awaiting trains, Rammone's
heart leaped to his mouth. But he grasped it and put marrow into
his bones, so that he might appear as one of the seasoned workers
of Johannesburg. He continued with all his preparations. Before
very long, after the electric trains had repeatedly snatched up and
gone off to disgorge their human freight, it arrived, the great black
ox of the government of Paul,[1] and it came treading slowly like a
pack-ox reluctant to take to the road. It spewed smoke on both
sides like a conceited man blowing tobacco-smoke through his
nostrils. . . .

In the late evening it made off, and traversed the great city amid
the glitter and twinkle of a myriad lights, until eventually it carried
the darkness on its head ; and the dust rose thickly and silence fell
on the passengers. Then could be heard only the metals of the
white man in dispute, the wheels railing at the rails, with a
rhythmic clatter — thatha — thatha — thatha — thatha — thatha —

[1] Paul Kruger, last President of the Transvaal Republic.

thatha. And so it spent the night in dispute with the darkness. When the sun showed its nose, it entered Mafeking.

When the big clocks boomed out the ninth hour, the train stood there in all its length, thronged by those who had come to bid farewell to friends going to the Protectorate. Then was heard the voice of the pot-bellied fellow who attended the passengers, calling 'All seats please—*sitplekke asseblief.*' . . . It jerked, did the black ox, and it wound out like a millipede, and left Mafeking behind. Quite soon it arrived at Lobatse, after winding itself in and out of the hills : the head would appear now on this side, now on that, as if it would go to touch the tail, or to ascertain whether the train officials, those pot-bellied fellows, were perhaps not asleep. . . .

The Committee is at the school.
We are plagued by Christians.[1]

[1] This country dance song is well-known in the Ndwedwe district of Natal.

The Dignity of Begging

WILLIAM MODISANE

THE magistrate raises his eyes above the documents and plunges them like daggers into my heart. His blue eyes are keen : my heart pounds like the bass of a boogie-woogie.

'I'm sick to death of you . . . heartily sick. There's not a native beggar on the streets whose full story I don't know,' the magistrate says. 'I've watched some of you grow up. There isn't one I haven't tried to rehabilitate many times. Some I was forced to send to gaol, but they always come back . . . they come back to the goose that lays the golden egg.'

These are fighting words. The magistrate sounds as though he's going to put us away for a few weeks. My only regret is that Richard Serurubele has to share my fate. If only the magistrate knew that he is not a parasite like the rest of us, that he's what is called an exploited beggar. He was crippled by an automobile accident, and since then his parents have made capital out of it. They use him to beg so they can balance the family budget. They never show him the comfort of love. Relentlessly they drive him, like an animal that has to work for its keep and feed. He is twenty-one. Dragging one foot along, he is an abject sight who has all the sadness of the world in his face. He looks many times older than my mother-in-law.

'You beggars make it difficult for me to do my duty, and in spite of my failure to rehabilitate you, I always believe in giving you another chance. . . . A fresh start, you might call it. But I'm almost certain that you'll be back here in a few days.'

The magistrate is getting soft, I can see my freedom at a distance of an arm's stretch. Here is my chance to put on my act. A look of deep compunction and a few well-chosen words can do the trick. I clear my throat and squeeze out a tear or two.

'Your honour, most of us beg because we've been ostracized by our families ; they treat us as though we were lepers,' I say, wiping off a tear. 'They want us to look up to them for all the things we need. They never encourage us to earn our own keep. Nobody wants to employ us, people are more willing to offer us alms rather than give us jobs. All they do is show us pity. . . . We don't want to be pitied, we want to be given a chance to prove that we're as good as anybody else.'

I can see from the silence in the court that everybody is deceived. . . . Everybody is filled with a sense of self-reproach. The magistrate is as mute as the undertaker's parlour. I can read pity on the faces of all the people in the court; perhaps the most pathetic is my own. I am magnificent. . . . an answer to every film director's dream. I know I have said enough . . . enough to let us out, that is.

'I understand you have matriculated, your name is Nathaniel, isn't it?' He turns a page of the report prepared by a worker in the Non-European Affairs Department. 'Yes, here we are. Nathaniel Mokgomare, the department recommends that you be sent to a place where you will be taught some useful trade. I want you to report to Room 14 at the department's building to-morrow morning.'

This is not what I had bargained for; my brilliant idea has boomeranged. Why must I take a job when I can earn twice a normal wage begging? After all, what will horses do if I take a job? I *must* uphold the dignity of begging. Professional ethics forbid all beggars from working.

'As for you, Richard Serurubele, I'll let you go this time, but mark my words: the next time you appear before me, I'll have you sent to the Bantu Refuge. Now get out of here, both of you.'

If the magistrate had seen the big grin on my face as we leave the court, he would have thrown my deformed carcass in gaol and deliberately lost the key. He does not see it though.

With the exception of a few loose ends everything has gone according to schedule, but my friend Serurubele is just about the most miserable man on earth. The trouble with him is he lacks imagination, but then of course, not everybody is as bright as I am. He always seems to be looking at the dull side of life, a vice coupled with an appalling brand of honesty most bishops would swear didn't exist.

'One of these days I'm going to kill myself,' Serurubele says. 'I can't go on like this, I'm tired of living off other people. Why did this have to happen to me? Tell me, Nathan. Why?'

How this man expects me to answer a question like this is beyond me. For one unguarded moment I almost tell him to send his Maker a telegram and ask Him all about it, but my gentler nature sees the harm such an answer might do.

'I don't know,' I say, abruptly. 'Things like this just happen; it's not in us to question why. Nature has a way of doing things, but even then she gives something in return. . . . at least I think so. . . . But how should I know, anyway?'

This is the one time I cannot find something concrete to say; I want to show him that there is compensation for his disability, but I just cannot lay my hands on it. This, I remember, is what made me leave home.

I left because my parents did not understand. They almost made a neurotic out of me; but to-day I wonder if it wasn't my own sensitivity which gave their actions then their seemingly absurd proportions. They seemed afraid to walk about freely; everybody sat down as if the house was full of cripples. I was treated like a babe in arms. All the things I wanted were brought to me, I was not even allowed to get myself water to drink. This excessive kindness gradually began to irritate me. . . . It became a constant reminder that I didn't belong, that I was an invalid. It then became apparent that they would soon put the food into my mouth which they had already chewed for me, and push it down my throat. These thoughts of inadequacy drove me from home.

A new life opened for me. I got myself a wife, two bouncing boys and a property at Pampoenfontein, also a room at Sophiatown complete with piano. Within two years I had begged well over a few hundred pounds. The money has been used wisely. Only one problem confronts me now, I want enough money to provide for my old age. . . . The two boys are also to be considered.

'For Christ's sake, Nathaniel,' Serurubele says, 'what's wrong with you. Why are you always so wrapped up in your thoughts. . . . this is where I stay, remember?'

I say good-bye to him and go to my room. After having something to eat I settle down to some hard thinking. There are all sorts of insurances and societies, unions and what have you, which protect workers. Why not a beggars' union? I could rally all the beggars of the city into one union with some professional name like 'The United Beggars' Union,' into whose funds every beggar would contribute ten shillings a week. In the city of Johannesburg alone, there are over a hundred beggars and if they could all be talked over, a capital of about two-thousand-four-hundred pounds could be realized in one year.

What a brilliant idea . . . an inspiration of genius. Sometimes I feel depressed that the world has not had the vision to realize the potentialities of my genius . . . possibly it cannot accommodate Einstein and myself in the same generation. Anyway, so much for that.

I could promise to offer each a bonus of ten pounds a year. That would be smart. . . . No beggar could resist such an offer. Maybe

I should promise to buy each a property somewhere cheap, say, buy one property a year for the needy ones like Serurubele, equip him with third-rate tools and interest him in turning out junk that nobody will care to give a second look at. The scheme would be costly, but at least it would go far in enlisting their confidence. Only one would get the property; the others would wait patiently until I get religion.

The following morning I'm at Room 14 bright and early. A white man with a bored expression on the face is sitting behind a big mahogany desk. I tell him my name. He takes some paper and writes on it. He tells me to go to the address written on the paper.

The faint showers that were falling outside have become heavier, and as I go out I say something nasty about the weather. A brilliant idea strikes me as a well-dressed lady is walking towards me. She looks like a mobile gold mine ready to be tapped. . . . in fact, I can almost see the gold nuggets in her teeth. I put on a gloomy face, bend lower than usual and let my deformed carcass shiver. She stops and looks at me as if she's responsible for my deformity.

'Why, you poor boy, you're freezing to death,' she says, with melodrama. 'Here, go buy yourself something to eat.'

I feel the half-crown piece in my hand and give her the usual line of how the good Lord will bless her, and send her tons and tons of luck: but from the way she's dressed, she appears to have had more than her share of luck.

I play this trick all the way to the address I'm given, and by the time I get there, I count well over ten half-crowns. Not bad, I say to myself; at this rate I can become the richest and most famous beggar in the city. To think the department wants to pin me behind a desk! The idea is criminal, to say the least.

One of these days when I'm on my annual leave, I hope to write a book on begging, something like a treatise on the subject. It will be written with sensitivity and charm, brimful with sketches from life, and profusely illustrated with coloured photographs, with easy-to-follow rules on the noblest and oldest occupation in the world: Begging! It will be a text-book for all aspiring beggars, young and old, who will reap a wealth of knowledge from my personal experiences and genius. In fact, I think it will be the only one of its kind in world literature. Even millionaires will take up begging as a pastime to colour their humdrum existence.

It will naturally begin with a history of the art from its ancient crudity of maiming children as a preparation in their education, right up to the contemporary age of beggars who are driven to the city in the latest American cars. . . . beggars with a bank balance big enough to impress the Receiver of Revenue. I can almost see it on the best seller list for several months. This reverie almost causes me to lose my way.

I find the place and go in. My heart just misses a beat when I see the large number of people inside. Some, if not most, are deformed monstrosities like myself. What could be sweeter? I can see my plan taking shape.

The man in charge starts explaining the elementary principles of the typewriter. I pretend to be interested and ask many unnecessary questions, but intelligent enough to impress him. By five o'clock I'm running over the keyboard like a brilliant amateur.

On my way home I go via Serurubele's corner. He is still there and looking as miserable as ever. I suggest that we go home. I lure him to my room and when we get there I begin playing a certain tarantella like Rubinstein, only my rendering is in a major flat. Either my piano recital is good or my friend just loves bad sounds.

'You can have a house like this and everything that goes with it; it's yours for the taking. Why beg for other people when you can do it for yourself?'

'I've got to help with the rent and the food,' he says. 'How do you think I'm going to get a house like this? I can't just wish for it.'

'You don't have to, you must plan and work for it like I did. I have a plan that will give it to you in less than a year. . . . Listen.'

I then start explaining to him about the society with particular emphasis on the good it will do to all beggars. I see his teeth sparkling behind thick lips. I put him in charge of organizing them for our first meeting.

Last night I dreamt I was at the race-course and I saw the winning double as plain as I see my twisted leg. I raid my savings in the room and make my way to Turffontein. When I get there I start scouting around for policemen. None are about and a soothing satisfaction comes with the realization that I shall not bother myself with police badges. I put a pound win on two and seven, a double in the first leg. As I'm making my bet, a man with eyes as big and lethargic as an owl's is standing next to me and beaming like a blushing groom.

I'm too nervous to watch the race, so I decide to walk about and appreciate the scenery. Suddenly I feel as though someone is staring at me. I turn round and look straight at Miss Gallovidian, a welfare worker, who has the uncanny habit of showing up at the most unexpected places. I don't need a fortune-teller to tell me I'm in trouble. She has a notorious record of having safely deposited more than twelve beggars in the Refuge. My only chance is to get out of here before she can find a beefy policeman. I'm walking to the gate when I hear people talking about two and seven. I even forget the trouble Miss Gallovidian is going to bring me. I run as fast as a man with a twisted leg can to the Bookie. Only six tickets were sold, the loud speaker was saying, only I'm not interested.

As the Bookie is handing me the money Blushing Groom seems even happier than I am. His crooked teeth, which are dulled by tobacco, click every time the Bookie counts a hundred. His greasy lips are watering while a pair of bloodshot eyes are blinking with a dull brilliance. It hurts my eyes to look at him. I have hardly put the money in my pocket, when gruesome pats me on the back and says, nice and loud : 'We made it !'

I must have been a fool not to have been wise as to why Blushing Groom was acting the perfect chaperon.

'That's fine,' I say. 'What have *we* made?'

'Don't be bashful,' he says, 'we caught the richest double. Come, this calls for a celebration.' He extends a hand, and all the time he's smiling as if his wife has given birth to quadruplets.

'Look, pal,' I say. 'It's a good try. I couldn't have done better myself. This is the perfect set-up, isn't it? Well, I've got news for you : I caught that double alone, I don't know you and I don't care to. Go get yourself another piece of cheese. . . . I'm not that easy.'

This ape suddenly stops smiling and looks at me like I had the plague. His broad, flat nose starts puffing out steam like an angry Spanish bull (only I'm not in the mood to make fancy passes like a toreador). All in all, he looks positively fierce, like the animal in the simile.

'Six-hundred and seventy pounds is a lot of money,' he shouts. 'Nobody's going to cheat me out of my share. You being a cripple. . . .'

'Shut up !' I yell. 'Never call me that again, you . . . You !' I swing a right cross to his face, but this ape is smart. He blocks it and lands a hard one on my chin. I rock back and land flat on my sitters, while jungle tom-toms beat out a solid conga in my head. After a while my head clears and I get up, burning with rage. If I only had the strength, I would tear this ape apart.

Blushing Groom has put on quite a show; we have a good audience. Some white folks are threatening to beat his brains out. . . . I sincerely hope they do.

Suddenly I see a police badge jostling its way through. This is no place for me ! I dash and start zigzagging through the people. A junior confusion starts, with everybody trying to give way. I run a few minutes, stumble and fall on my face. The policeman bends down and grabs me firmly by the arm and whispers : 'Look, John, let's not have trouble. Come along quietly and everything will be just fine.'

Under the circumstances I have no choice but to submit. My mother always told me never to resist arrest, let alone striking a uniformed officer of the law. Me and my money part company after Blushing Groom had preferred charges. My submission causes me to spend a not-so-glorious week-end at the Bantu Refuge. My transfer there being arranged by the thoughtful sergeant in the charge office, who out of pure love could not have me thrown in with hardened criminals. . . . what with the place filled with house-breakers, extortioners, professional pick-pockets and a generous assortment of other unsavoury characters. Frankly, I hoped he would mind his own business. I might even have started a crap game and made me some money.

'I am almost certain that you will be back here in a few days,' the magistrate had said. Somebody ought to tell him he has a great future . . . reading palms. He looks at me and a grin spreads over his pancake-like face. This place must be short of magistrates ; why has it got to be the same one all the time?

'Beggars who play the horses are a dangerous nuisance. They misuse the kindness that is shown to them.'

Just my luck : now I have to listen to a lecture on morals. The magistrate looks pleased with himself, and I don't like it. Miss Gallovidian looks at me and smiles like a proud victress. She probably expects a promotion for this. I'm called on to the stand.

Some man with a thin face asks me to raise my right hand and swear to tell the truth. After saying my piece, the prosecutor starts questioning me as if he's promised thirty per cent of Blushing Groom's cut. After his session with me, he calls Blushing Groom to the stand.

'Do you know this man?' the prosecutor says.

'No, sir.'

'How was it then you put up ten shillings to bet the horses with him?'

'I was losing all morning when I decided to try somebody's guesses. I met him, and we started talking.'

'Did anybody see you talking to him?'

'I don't know, but somebody must have.'

'Then what happened?'

'I asked him if he had a tip. He said he had one straight from the horse's mouth. . . A sure thing, he said. I then asked him if I could put up ten shillings. He agreed. I was afraid to make the bet, so I gave him the money and walked over to the Bookie's stand with him where he placed a pound win on two and seven.'

'Why were you afraid to make the bet?'

'I thought he was luckier than I was. . . . besides, I had been losing all morning.'

'Why did you strike him?'

'He was trying to cheat me out of my share, and tried to hit me when he couldn't.'

The magistrate looks at me with something like contempt in his eyes. I won't have to put on a show for him this time. I might just as well kiss half my money good-bye. Blushing Groom's story is water-tight.

'I'm thoroughly disappointed with you,' the magistrate says. 'I didn't know you were a thief too. I don't believe you could have made that bet alone; beggars haven't got so much money. I believe his story, things like this do happen. The money will be shared equally between the two of you.'

'I don't believe you could have made that bet alone.' What a cheek! I'll have that hobo know I make more money in one week than he does in a month. I don't believe you. . . . Good God!

I feel like committing mass murder as the court hands Blushing Groom three hundred and thirty-five pounds of my money. This prehistoric beast has a swell racket. A few more jobs like this and he can retire and buy himself a villa on the Riviera.

Blushing Groom is magnificent, inspiring awe. He is completely uncompromising, thoroughly unscrupulous, without qualms or a conscience. He has wholly realized the separateness of good and evil and attained a purity in evil worthy of honest appraisal. He would not allow himself to be swayed from cheating me by my being a cripple. If I were allowed to choose a brother, he would be my only choice.

I take my share of the money and clear out before the magistrate and Miss Gallovidian cook up another charge against me. On my way home I find it difficult to resist the temptation of stopping at some busy corner and doing my stuff. I might make up for some of the money, but I just happen to be wearing my best and have been a beggar long enough to know that people don't give money away to beggars who are dressed better than they. People who give alms to beggars do so to establish their superiority over the receiver, and like I said : I'm not an apprentice beggar.

When I get home I find a letter from my wife.

'Our son, Tommy, is sick. Please come home. . . .'

I become afraid and anxious for my Tommy, and even the kind words of my outsize landlady fail to move me.

I had to wait for something like this to show me the folly of my ways. A man's place is next to his wife and family. I had hoped that some day I would be able to provide my boys with a decent education, to grow them like normal boys, not just sons of a helpless cripple. . . . to find a place for them in the sun. I might be a big shot beggar but as a husband and father, I stink.

'If I should not see my friend Serurubele, will you. . . .'

'Yes, I'll explain to him. I'll always have your room for you if you should ever want it again.'

Deep down I know that I will want it again. I have three hundred and thirty-five reasons why I should. Blushing Groom and the gullible public of Johannesburg will live in my mind for ever. . . . I have to come back. I owe it to the profession.

Take off your hat.
What is your home name?
Who is your father?
Who is your chief?
Where do you pay your tax?
What river do you drink?
We mourn for our country.[1]

The Bench

RICHARD RIVE

'WE form an integral part of a complex society, a society complex in that a vast proportion of the population are denied the very basic privileges of existence, a society that condemns a man to an inferior position because he has the misfortune to be born black, a society that can only retain its precarious social and economic position at the expense of an enormous oppressed proletariat!'

Karlie's eyes shone as he watched the speaker. Those were great words, he thought, great words and true. The speaker paused for

[1] The scene is any pass office, where all male Africans must go to get their Registration Certificates. There they may wait in queues for hours and sometimes for days before they are attended to. It is a regulation which rankles in their minds and so they sing about it.

a moment and sipped some water from a glass. Karlie sweated. The hot October sun beat down mercilessly on the gathering. The trees on the Grand Parade afforded very little shelter and his handkerchief was already soaked where he had placed it between his neck and shirt collar. Karlie stared round him at the sea of faces. Every shade of colour was represented, from shiny ebony to the one or two whites in the crowd. He stared at the two detectives who were busily making shorthand notes of the speeches, and then turned to stare back at the speaker.

'It is up to us to challenge the rights of any groups who wilfully and deliberately condemn a fellow group to a servile position. We must challenge the rights of any people who see fit to segregate human beings solely on grounds of pigmentation. Your children are denied the rights which are theirs by birth. They are segregated socially, economically . . . .'

Ah, thought Karlie, that man knows what he is speaking about. He says I am as good as any other man, even a white man. That needs much thinking. I wonder if he thinks I have the right to go into any bioscope or eat in any restaurant, or that my children can go to any school? These are dangerous ideas and need much thinking; I wonder what Ou Klaas would say to this. Ou Klaas said God made the white man and the black man separately and the one must always be '*baas*' [1] and the other '*jong*.' [2] But this man says different things and somehow they seem true.

Karlie's brow was knitted as he thought. On the platform were many speakers, both white and black, and they were behaving as if there were no difference of colour between them. There was a white woman in a blue dress offering a cigarette to Nxeli. That could never happen at Bietjiesvlei. Old Lategan at the store would have fainted if his Annatjie had offered Witbooi a cigarette. And Annatjie had no such pretty dress. These were new things, and he, Karlie, had to be careful before he accepted them. But why shouldn't he accept them? He was not coloured any more, he was a human being. The speaker had said so. He remembered seeing pictures in the newspaper of people who defied laws which relegated them to a particular class, and those people were smiling as they went to prison. This was a strange world.

The speaker continued and Karlie listened intently. His speech was obviously carefully prepared and he spoke slowly, choosing his words. This is a great man, Karlie thought.

The last speaker was the white lady in the blue dress, who asked them to challenge any discriminatory laws or measures in every

[1] Master.
[2] Boy.

possible manner. Why should she speak like that? thought Karlie. She could go to the best bioscopes, and swim at the best beaches. Why, she was even more beautiful than Annatjie Lategan. They had warned him in Bietjiesvlei about coming to the city. He had seen the *Skollies* [1] in District Six and knew what to expect there. Hanover Street held no terrors for him. But no one had told him about this. This was new, this set one's mind thinking, yet he felt it was true. She said one should challenge. He would challenge. He, Karlie, would astound old Lategan and Balie at the dairy farm. They could do what they liked to him after that. He would smile like those people in the newspaper.

The meeting was almost over when Karlie threaded his way through the crowd. The words of the speakers were still milling through his head. It could never happen in Bietjiesvlei, he thought, or could it? The sudden screech of a car pulling to a hurried stop whirled him back to his senses. A white head was angrily thrust through the window. 'Look where you're going, you black bastard!'

Karlie stared dazedly at him. Surely this white man had never heard what the speakers had said. He could never have seen the white woman offering Nxeli a cigarette. Karlie could never imagine the white lady shouting those words at him. It would be best to catch a train and think these things over.

He saw the station in a new light. Here was a mass of human beings, some black, some white, and some brown like himself. Here they mixed with one another, yet each mistrusted the other with an unnatural fear. Each treated the other with suspicion, each moved in a narrow, haunted pattern of its own manufacture. One must challenge these things the speaker had said . . . in one's own way. Yet how in one's own way? How was one to challenge? Slowly it dawned upon him. Here was his chance, *the bench*. The railway bench with the legend 'Europeans Only' neatly painted on it in white. For one moment it symbolized all the misery of the plural South African society. Here was a challenge to his rights as a man. There it stood, a perfectly ordinary wooden railway bench, like hundreds of thousands of others in South Africa. His challenge. That bench, now, had concentrated in it all the evils of a system he could not understand. It was the obstacle between himself and humanity. If he sat on it he was a man. If he was afraid he denied himself membership as a human in a human society. He almost had visions of righting the pernicious system if only he sat on that bench. Here was his chance. He, Karlie, would challenge.

He seemed perfectly calm when he sat down on the bench, but inside his heart was thumping wildly. Two conflicting ideas now

[1] Thugs.

throbbed through him. The one said, 'I have no right to sit on this bench'; the other said, 'Why have I no right to sit on this bench?' The one voice spoke of the past, of the servile position he had occupied on the farms, of his father and his father's father who were born black, lived like blacks and died like oxen. The other voice spoke of the future and said, 'Karlie you are a man. You have dared what your father would not have dared. You will die like a man!'

Karlie took out a cigarette and smoked. Nobody seemed to notice his sitting there. This was an anti-climax. The world still pursued its monotonous way. No voice shouted 'Karlie has conquered!' He was a normal human being sitting on a bench on a busy station, smoking a cigarette. Or was this his victory, the fact that he was a normal human being? A well-dressed white woman walked down the platform. Would she sit on the bench, Karlie wondered. And then that gnawing voice, 'You should stand and let the white woman sit.' Karlie narrowed his eyes and gripped tighter at his cigarette. She swept past him without the slightest twitch of an eyelid and walked on down the platform. Was she afraid to challenge, to challenge his right to be a human? Karlie now felt tired. A third conflicting emotion was now creeping in, a compensatory emotion which said, 'You do not sit on this bench to challenge, you sit there because you are tired. You are tired; therefore you sit.' He would not move because he was tired, or was it because he wanted to sit where he liked?

People were now pouring out of a train that had pulled into the station. There were so many people pushing and jostling one another that nobody noticed him. This was his train. It would be quite easy to step into the train and ride off home, but that would be giving in, suffering defeat, refusing the challenge, in fact admitting that he was not a human being. He sat on. Lazily he blew the cigarette smoke into the air, thinking . . . his mind was far from the meeting and the bench, he was thinking of Bietjiesvlei and Ou Klaas, how he had insisted that Karlie should come to Cape Town. Ou Klaas could look so quizzically at one and suck at his pipe. He was wise to know and knew much. He had said one must go to Cape Town and learn the ways of the world. He would spit and wink slyly when he spoke of District Six and the women he knew in Hanover Street. Ou Klaas knew everything. He said God made us white or black and we must therefore keep our places.

'Get off this seat!'

Karlie did not hear the gruff voice. Ou Klaas would be on the land now, waiting for his tot of cheap wine.

'I said get off the bench, you swine!'

61

Karlie suddenly whipped back to reality. For a moment he was going to jump up, then he remembered who he was and why he was sitting there. Suddenly he felt very tired. He looked up slowly into a very red face that stared down at him.

'Get up! I said, there are benches down there for you!'

Karlie stared up and said nothing. He stared up into very sharp, cold grey eyes.

'Can't you hear me speaking to you, you black swine!'

Slowly and deliberately Karlie puffed at his cigarette. So this was his test. They both stared at each other, challenged with the eyes, like two boxers, each knowing that they must eventually trade blows yet each afraid to strike first.

'Must I dirty my hands on scum like you?'

Karlie said nothing. To speak would be to break the spell, the supremacy he felt he was slowly gaining. An uneasy silence. Then,

'I will call a policeman rather than kick a Hotnot[1] like you! You can't even open your black jaw when a white man speaks to you!'

Karlie saw the weakness. The white youth was afraid to take action himself. He, Karlie, had won the first round of the bench dispute!

A crowd now collected. 'Afrika!' shouted one joker. Karlie ignored the remark. People were now milling around, staring at the unusual sight of a black man sitting on a white man's bench. Karlie merely puffed on.

'Look at the black ape! That's the worst of giving these Kaffirs too much rope!'

'I can't understand it, they have their own benches!'

'Don't get up, you have every right to sit there!'

'He'll get hell when a policeman comes!'

'Mind you, I can't see why they shouldn't sit where they please!'

'I've said before, I've had a native servant, and a more impertinent . . . .'

Karlie sat and heard nothing. Irresolution had now turned to determination. Under no condition was he going to rise. They could do what they liked.

'So this is the fellow, hey, get up there! Can't you read?' The policeman was towering over him. Karlie could see the crest on his buttons and the thin wrinkles on his neck.

'What is your name and address?'

Karlie still maintained his obstinate silence. It took the policeman rather unawares. The crowd was growing every minute.

[1] Hottentot.

'You have no right to speak to this man in such a manner!' It was the white lady in the blue dress.

'Mind your own business! I'll ask your help when I need it. It is people like you who make Kaffirs think they're as good as white people!'

Then addressing Karlie, 'Get up, you!'

'I insist that you treat him with proper respect!'

The policeman turned red. 'This . . . this . . . .' He was at a loss for words.

'Kick up the Hotnot if he won't get up!' shouted a spectator. Rudely a white man laid hands on Karlie. 'Get up you bloody bastard!'

Karlie turned to resist, to cling to the bench, his bench. There were more than one man now pulling at him. He hit out wildly and then felt a dull pain as somebody rammed a fist into his face. He was now bleeding and wild-eyed. He would fight for it. The constable clapped a pair of handcuffs round Karlie's wrists and tried to clear a way through the crowds. Karlie was still struggling. A blow or two landed on him. Suddenly he relaxed and slowly struggled to his feet. It was useless fighting any longer. Now it was his turn to smile. He had challenged and won. Who cared at the result?

'Come on, you swine!' said the policeman, forcing Karlie through the crowd.

'Certainly,' said Karlie for the first time, and stared at the policeman with the arrogance of one who dared to sit on a 'European' bench.

Ethiopia

※

Trousers of Wind

※

A household song about a worthless lover, sung by the women
as they work

Translated from the Amharic by Sylvia Pankhurst
assisted by Ato Menghestu Lemma

> Trousers of wind and buttons of hail;
> A lump of Shoa earth, at Gondar nothing left;
> A hyena bearing meat, led by a leather thong;
> Some water in a glass left standing by the fire;
> A measure of water thrown on the hearth;
> A horse of mist and a swollen ford;
> Useless for anything, useful to no one;
> Why am I in love with such a man as he?

The Queen of Sheba

Translated by Sir E. A. Wallis Budge from Ishak's ancient Ethiopic
version of the 'Kebra Nagast' (The Glory of Kings)
and adapted by Sylvia Pankhurst

Introductory note : The Ethiopians claim that their Queen Makeda was the
Queen of Sheba who journeyed to Jerusalem to seek the wisdom of
Solomon. Here she tells of the wisdom she found there.

I WENT in through the doors of the treasury of wisdom, and I
drew for myself the waters of understanding. I went into the blaze
of the flame of the sun, and it lighted me with the splendour
thereof ; and I made of it a shield for myself, and I saved myself
by confidence therein ; and not myself only, but all those who
travel in the footprints of wisdom ; and not myself only, but all the
men of my country, the Kingdom of Ethiopia ; and not those only,
but the nations that are round about. . . .

Through wisdom I have dived down into the great sea, and have
seized in the place of her depths a pearl whereby I am rich. I went
down like the great iron anchor, whereby men anchor ships for the
night on the high seas, and I received a lamp which lighteth me,
and I came up by the ropes of the boat of understanding.

'The guest is first gold, then silver and finally iron.' [1]

---

[1] Translated from the Amharic by Professor Murad Kamel.

Justice

An Ethiopian Tale

Told to Wolf Leslau by a student of the Teachers' Training School in Addis Ababa

A WOMAN one day went out to look for her goats that had wandered away from the herd. She walked back and forth over the fields for a long time without finding them. She came at last to a place by the side of the road where a deaf man sat before a fire brewing himself a cup of coffee. Not realizing he was deaf, the woman asked :

'Have you seen my herd of goats come this way?'

The deaf man thought she was asking for the water hole, so he pointed vaguely toward the river.

The woman thanked him and went to the river. And there, by coincidence, she found the goats. But a young kid had fallen among the rocks and broken its foot.

She picked it up to carry it home. As she passed the place where the deaf man sat drinking his coffee, she stopped to thank him for his help. And in gratitude she offered him the kid.

But the deaf man didn't understand a word she was saying. When she held the kid toward him he thought she was accusing him of the animal's misfortune, and he became very angry.

'I had nothing to do with it !' he shouted.

'But you pointed the way,' the woman said.

'It happens all the time with goats !' the man shouted.

'I found them right where you said they would be,' the woman replied.

'Go away and leave me alone, I never saw him before in my life !' the man shouted.

People who came along the road stopped to hear the argument.

The woman explained to them :

'I was looking for the goats and he pointed toward the river. Now I wish to give him this kid.'

67

'Do not insult me in this way!' the man shouted loudly. 'I am not a leg breaker!' And in his anger he struck the woman with his hand.

'Ah, did you see? He struck me with his hand!' the woman said to the people. 'I will take him before the judge!'

So the woman with the kid in her arms, the deaf man, and the spectators went to the house of the judge. The judge came out before his house to listen to their complaint. First, the woman talked, then the man talked, then people in the crowd talked. The judge sat nodding his head. But that meant very little, for the judge, like the man before him, was very deaf. Moreover, he was also very nearsighted.

At last, he put up his hand and the talking stopped. He gave them his judgment.

'Such family rows are a disgrace to the Emperor and an affront to the Church,' he said solemnly. He turned to the man.

'From this time forward, stop mistreating your wife,' he said.

He turned to the woman with the young goat in her arms.

'As for you, do not be so lazy. Hereafter do not be late with your husband's meals.'

He looked at the baby goat tenderly.

'And as for the beautiful infant, may she have a long life and grow to be a joy to you both!'

The crowd broke up and the people went their various ways.

'Ah, how good it is!' they said to each other. 'How did we ever get along before justice was given to us?'

Hymn of Praise

Translated from the Ethiopic by Sir E. A. Wallis Budge and adapted by Sylvia Pankhurst

I T[1] is not gold and silver I offer unto thee, nor the brilliant pearl, but beautiful praise and the pure glorification which can be offered to thee and thy Majesty, O Queen. Not purple robes of honour I offer thee, nor cloths of silk brocade adorned with divers colours:

[1] The 'Arganona Waddase,' from which this is an extract, is one of the most popular Ethiopian hymns of praise to the Virgin Mary.

I lay out my soul in place of glorious apparel decorated with gold, and to thee I declare my sin, O Mother of the Great High Priest. I have found thee a refuge from the corruption which is on the earth and from the punishment which endures for ever, a refuge from the lions of the north which mightily roar, which snatch away with violence, and hunt the young and show no mercy to the old. Who can strike terror into him who putteth trust in thy name? The roaring of the lion one may liken to the yelp of the dog, the strength of the panther is to him as the feebleness of the cat. The flooding of the rivers cannot overwhelm him; the violence of the winds cannot cast him down.

I rejoice in thy love in the salvation of Christ, thy son. The extent and height of thy love is in the fortress of my being; it hath filled me like the overflow of a river, like the river Nile in the days of winter, and in the days of the flowers, like the river Tigris in the days of harvest, and the river Euphrates when the Tigris wheat is in the ear, like the river Efeson at the time of the flowering of the vines. And thy love hath spread itself out in me like the mist on the face of the earth, and like the descent of a cloud in the air. Thou hast been my adornment in my happiness, and become to me a crown in my joy.

How the Ethiopian Woman Tamed her Husband

Based on an Ethiopian tale
re-told by Professor Murad Kamel

ONCE there was a woman who was greatly troubled by her husband. He no longer loved her. He neglected her and seemed to care little whether she was happy or sad.

So the woman took her troubles to the local witchdoctor. She told him her story, full of pity for herself and her sad plight. 'Can you give me a charm to make him love me again?' she asked anxiously.

The witchdoctor thought for a moment and replied. 'I will help you, but first you must bring to me three hairs from the mane of a living lion. These I must have before I can make the charm for you.'

The woman thanked the witchdoctor and went away. When she came near to her home she sat down on a rock and began to think, 'How shall I do this thing? There is a lion who comes often near to my village, it is true. But he is fierce and roars fearfully.' Then she thought again and at last she knew what she would do.

And so, rising early next morning she took a young lamb and went to the place where the lion was accustomed to stroll about. She waited anxiously. At last she saw the lion approaching. Now was the time. Quickly she rose and, leaving the lamb in the path of the lion, she went home. And so it was that every day early in the morning the woman would arise and take a young lamb to the lion. Soon the lion came to know the woman, for she was always in the same place at the same time every day with a young and tender lamb, which she brought for his pleasure. She was indeed a kind and attentive woman.

It was not long before the lion began to wag his tail each time he saw her and coming close to her he would let her stroke his head and soothe his back. And each day the woman would stay quietly stroking the lion, gently and lovingly. Then one day when she knew that the lion trusted her she carefully pulled three hairs from his mane and happily set out for the witchdoctor's dwelling.

'See,' she said triumphantly as she entered, 'here they are!' And she gave him the three hairs from the lion's mane.

'How is it you have been so clever?' asked the witchdoctor in amazement.

And so the woman told him the story of how she had patiently won the hairs from the lion.

A smile spread over the face of the witchdoctor and, leaning forward, he said, 'In the same way that you have tamed the lion, so may you tame your husband.'

East Africa

The Story of Liongo

Told by

HAMISI WA KAYI OF ZANZIBAR

Translated from the Swahili by Edward Steere

❀

Editor's note: About 'The Story of Liongo,' Edward Steere, that great Bishop of Central Africa, writes in 1869: 'No one has any clear notion how long ago it is since Liongo died, but his memory is warmly cherished, and it is wonderful how the mere mention of his name rouses the interest of almost any true Swahili.'

I N the times when Shanga [1] was a flourishing city, there was a man whose name was Liongo, and he had great strength, and was a very great man in the city. And he oppressed the people exceedingly, till one day they made a plan to go to him to his house and bind him. And a great number of people went and came upon him suddenly into his house, and seized him and bound him, and went with him to the prison, and put him into it.

And he stayed many days, and made a plot to get loose. And he went outside the town and harassed the people in the same way for many days. People could not go into the country, neither to cut wood nor to draw water. And they were in much trouble.

And the people said, 'What stratagem can we resort to, to get him and kill him?' And one said, 'Let us go against him while he is sleeping, and kill him out of the way.' Others said, 'If you get him, bind him and bring him.' And they went and made a stratagem so as to take him, and they bound him with chains and fetters and a post between his legs.

And they left him many days, and his mother used to send him food every day. And before the door where he was bound soldiers were set, who watched him; they never went away except by turns.

---

[1] Shanga is said to have been destroyed by Sultan Omar bin Muhammad of Pate during the fourteenth century.—Dr. A. Werner.

73

Many days and many months had passed. Every day, night by night, he used to sing beautiful songs; every one who heard them used to be delighted with those songs. Every one used to say to his friend, 'Let us go and listen to Liongo's songs, which he sings in his room.' And they used to go and say to him, 'We have come to sing your songs, let us hear them.' And he used to sing, he could not refuse, and the people in the town were delighted with them. And every day he composed different ones, through his grief at being bound. Till the people knew those songs little by little, but he and his mother and her slave knew them well. And his mother knew the meaning of those songs, and the people of the town did not.

At last one day their slave girl had brought some food, and the soldiers took it from her and ate it, and some scraps were left, and those they gave her. The slave girl told her master, 'I brought food, and these soldiers have taken it from me and eaten it; there remain these scraps.' And he said to her, 'Give me them.' And he received them and ate, and thanked God for what he had got.

And he said to the slave girl (and he was inside and the slave girl outside the door)—'You, slave girl, shall be sent to tell my mother I am a simpleton. I have not yet learnt the ways of the world. Let her make a cake, in the middle let be put files, that I may cut my fetters, and the chains may be opened, that I may enter the road, that I may glide like a snake, that I may mount the roofs and walls, that I may look this way and that.'

And he said, 'Greet my mother well, tell her what I have told you.' And she went and told his mother, and said, 'Your son greets you well, he has told me a message to come and tell you.' And she said, 'What message?' And she told her what she had been told.

And his mother understood it, and went away to a shop and exchanged for grain, and gave it to her slave to clean. And she went and bought many files, and brought them. And she took the flour, and made many fine cakes. And she took the bran and made a large cake, and took the files and put them into it, and gave it to her slave to take to him.

And she went with them, and arrived at the door, and the soldiers robbed her, and chose out the fine cakes, and ate them themselves. And as for the bran one, they told her to take that to her master. And she took it, and he broke it, and took out the files, and laid them away, and ate that cake and drank water, and was comforted.

And the people of the town wished that he should be killed. And he heard himself that it was said, 'You shall be killed.' And he said to the soldiers, 'When shall I be killed?' And they told him, 'To-morrow.' And he said, 'Call me my mother, and the chief man

74

in the town, and all the townspeople, that I may take leave of them.'

And they went and called them, and many people came together, and his mother and her slave.

And he asked them, 'Are you all assembled?' And they answered, 'We are assembled.' And he said, 'I want a horn, and cymbals, and an *upato*.' [1] And they went and took them. And he said, 'I have an entertainment to-day, I want to take leave of you.' And they said to him, 'Very well, go on, play.' And he said, 'Let one take the horn, and one take the cymbals, and one take the *upato*.' And they said, 'How shall we play them?' And he taught them to play, and they played.

And he himself there, where he was inside, sang, till when the music was in full swing, he took a file and cut his fetters. When the music dropped, he too left off and sang, and when they played he cut his fetters.

And the people knew nothing of what was going on inside till the fetters were divided, and he cut the chains till they were divided. And the people knew nothing of it through their delight in the music. When they looked up, he had broken the door and come out to them outside. And they threw their instruments away to run, without being quick enough; and he caught them and knocked their heads together and killed them. And he went outside the town, and took leave of his mother, 'to see one another again.'

And he went away into the forest, and stayed many days harassing people as before, and killing people.

And they sent crafty men, and told them, 'Go and make him your friend, so as to kill him.' And they went fearingly. And when they arrived they made a friendship with him. Till one day they said to him, 'Sultan, let us entertain one another.' And Liongo answered them, 'If I eat of an entertainment, what shall I give in return, I who am excessively poor?' And they said to him, 'Let us entertain one another with koma fruit.' And he asked them, 'How shall we eat them?' And they said, 'One shall climb into the koma tree, and throw them down for us to eat. When we have done, let another climb up, till we have finished.' And he said to them, 'Very well.'

And the first climbed up, and they ate. And the second climbed up, and they ate. And the third climbed up and they ate. And they had plotted that when Liongo should climb up, 'Let us shoot him with arrows there, up above.'

But Liongo saw through it by his intelligence. So when all had finished they said to him, 'Come, it is your turn.' And he said,

[1] A plate of metal beaten with a stick.

75

'Very well.' And he took his bow in his hand, and his arrows, and said, 'I will strike the ripe above, that we may eat in the midst.' And he shot, and a bough was broken off; and he shot again, and a second was broken off; and he stripped a whole koma tree, and the ground was covered with fruit. And they ate. And when they had done, the men said among themselves, 'He has seen through it; now what are we to do?' And they said, 'Let us go away.' And they took leave of him and said, 'Liongo the chief, you have not been taken in; you are not a man, you have got out of it like a devil.'

And they went away and gave their answer to their head-man there in the town, and said, 'We could do nothing.'

And they advised together, 'Who will be able to kill him?' And they said, 'Perhaps his nephew will.' And they went and called him. And he came. And they said to him, 'Go and ask your father what it is that will kill him. When you know, come and tell us, and when he is dead we will give you the kingdom.' And he answered them, 'Very well.'

And he went. When he arrived he welcomed him and said, 'What have you come to do?' And he said. 'I have come to see you.' And he said, 'I know that you have come to kill me, and they have deceived you.'

And he asked him, 'Father, what is it that can kill you?' And he said, 'A copper needle.[1] If any one stabs me in the navel, I die.'

And he went away into the town, and answered them and said, 'It is a copper needle that will kill him.' And they gave him a needle, and he went back to his father. And when he saw him, his father sang, and said, 'I, who am bad, am he that is good to you; do me no evil. I that am bad, am he that is good to you.' And he welcomed him, and he knew, 'He is come to kill me.'

And he stayed two days, till one day he was asleep in the evening, and he stabbed him with the needle in the navel. And he awoke through the pain, and took his bow and arrows and went to a place near the wells. And he knelt down, and put himself ready with his bow. And there he died.

So in the morning the people who came to draw water saw him, and they thought him alive, and went back running. And they gave out the news in the town : 'No water is to be had to-day.' Every one that went came back running. And many people set out and went, and as they arrived, when they saw him they came back, without being able to get near. For three days the people were in distress for water, not getting any.

And they called his mother, and said to her, 'Go and speak to

[1] A large copper needle is always used for the sewing together of mats.

your son, that he may go away and we get water, or we will kill you.'

And she went till she reached him. And his mother took hold of him to soothe him with songs, and he fell down. And his mother wept; she knew her son was dead.

And she went to tell the townspeople that he was dead, and they went to look at him, and saw that he was dead, and buried him, and his grave is to be seen at Ozi to this day.

And they seized that young man and killed him, and did not give him the kingdom.

The Monkey who left his Heart in a Tree

Told by

HAMISI WA KAYI

Translated from the Swahili by Edward Steere

THERE was once a monkey which made friends with a shark. There was a great tree, of the sort called mkuyu, which grew near the deep water; half its branches were over the town and half over the sea. The monkey used to go every day and eat the kuyu fruit, and his friend the shark was there under the tree. He used to say, 'Throw me some food, my friend'; and he used to throw to him, many days and many months.

Till one day the shark said to the monkey, 'You have done me many kindnesses, I should like for us to go to my home, that I may repay you for your kindness.'

The monkey answered him, 'How shall I go? We don't go into the water, we beasts of the land.'

And he said, 'I will carry you; not a drop of water shall get to you.'

And he said, 'Let us go.'

They went half the way. And the shark said, 'You are my friend, I will tell you the truth.'

He said, 'Tell me.'

He said, 'There, at home, where we are going, our Sultan is very ill, and we have been told that the medicine for him is a monkey's heart.'

The monkey replied to him, 'You did not do well not to tell me there on the spot.'

The shark said, 'How so?'

The monkey considered, and felt, 'My life is gone already; now I will tell him a lie, perhaps that may serve me.'

The shark asked him, 'You have become silent; don't you speak?'

He said, 'I have nothing to say, because of your not telling me there on the spot, and I might have brought my heart.'

The shark asked, 'Have you your heart here?'

'Don't you know about us? When we go out we leave our hearts in the trees, and we go about with only our bodies; but you won't believe me, you will tell me I am afraid; let us go on now to your home there, and kill me if you find my heart.'

The shark believed it, and said to the monkey, 'Let us go back now, and you get your heart.'

The monkey said, 'I don't agree to that, but let us go to your place.'

And he said, 'Let us go back first and take your heart, that we may go on.'

The monkey considered—I had better consent to him as far as to the tree; I know what to do when I have got there. They went and returned to the tree, and the monkey climbed up and said, 'Wait for me here, shark, I am going to get my heart, that we may be off.'

He climbed into the tree and sat down quite still. The shark called him. He held his tongue.

He called him again and said, 'Let us be going.'

The monkey answered him, 'Let us go where?'

He said, 'Let us go to our home.'

So the monkey said to the shark, 'Take your way and be off home, you are not going to get me again, and our friendship is ended. Good-bye.'

The Story of a Bemba Slave Boy

Translated from the Swahili by A. C. Madan

🜲

This true story of slavery was written by a young Bemba boy. It is one of several written in the 1880s by African boys at the schools of the Universities' Mission to Central Africa in Zanzibar, where they were taken after they had been rescued from slavery. Almost all of them were captured from slave ships by British cruisers on the east coast of Africa.

SINCE I left my own land,[1] and, indeed, since I was born, I never saw or knew my mother. I lived with one of my mother's relations. He brought me up, till I was about eight years old, and after a time they said, 'Now we are going to travel and join our other people.' So we started. It was because there was a war very near us, but we escaped, sir, and got safe to a country, where was a chief, and this chief's name was Mweenge. There we lived, in the same place as others of our tribe.

One day, when it was time for us to go home again, we started and travelled for three days, and then slept in a very large hut. Here the Magwangwara came upon the hut. I had gone into the fields to play and look for something to eat with a man whose name was Kipofu, and the older women of the family were left in the hut. Well, in the evening, the Magwangwara came, and we were in the fields, and we heard the cries of the people, and the houses burning with fire. We ran away to get to the village, and found nothing but men's heads. Then we cried till we were tired, and then climbed up into a tree and slept. In the morning we woke up, and considered, and said, 'Well, where are we to go now? We have not got a morsel of food.' All I had with me was a little basket. Then we went back, and found a garden which had been planted with ground nuts, but they had been dug up. However, we went and picked up a few nuts, about ten apiece. The house to which the garden belonged was on a little hill, and the people saw us, and came down to catch us. My companion heard then coming running down, and he ran away as fast as ever he could, and the people

[1] The Bemba people live to the westward of Lake Nyassa.

79

came and caught me. And I thought, 'This man will make me his slave.' I stayed there thirty-two days, and then he sold me for just seven hoes.

My new master carried me off, and they took me to their town called Malani, and there I stayed a month, and my master got into trouble, because of a man who accused him of witchcraft. They took the omens about him, but the omens did not convict him. Next they carried me away to Bisaland, and there I met Mpunga. I remained there with my mistress, whose name was Namlia Isani. Then some Arabs came there, bringing their cloth, and the people sold me and Mpunga too.

The Arab was a very cruel man, and he had a great many slaves. There were thirty-one. Then we came to Yaoland, to the country of a chief called Makanjila. There we settled, and grew crops of millet and maize, and ground nuts, and food of many kinds, remaining there a great many months. When we had finished eating all our crops, the Arabs made up a very large caravan, and we came to a town called Akasunga. But we did not stay there; we started off and came to Kilwa, and there we stayed. My master sold me to another Arab, me and Mpunga and another, and we were sent by the Arab to carry rice to the encampment. We carried the rice and went off, and when we got there we found a great number of Arabs and others, among them Taisiri. And all the people we were with had a very heavy chain.

There were two dhows there, one smaller than the other, but sailing faster than the one we got into. When we got into the dhow, it was quite night time, perhaps the time we go to evening service— 8.30 p.m.—and when we went into the water it came up to our necks. Then we got into the dhow and were arranged in order, and the Arabs weighed the anchor, and we put out to sea, and lay down for three or four days. It was a very large number of people who went on board, with goats, and fowls, and a large stock of food. But the Arabs were very cruel during the voyage, and because we were in a dhow we were told that the Europeans were bad people, but we thought, 'Never mind, they can't be worse than you. You torment us for nothing.' One night a child in the dhow cried very much, and the Arabs were just going to kill it, but one Arab said, 'Never mind; let it alone. We are nearly there.' So they let it alone, but when it was four o'clock in the morning we heard a cannon-shot over the sail, and the Arabs cried 'Oh! ah! the English!' When the English boarded the dhow, every one said, 'I am a slave, sir.' [1] For when we were caught by the English, we were glad. But

[1] This case was unusual. As a rule one of the chief difficulties of an English officer on boarding a dhow suspected of carrying slaves was the

when I thought about my home, I cried. But still, because slavery up the country is a very hard life, and because we do not know about God there—yet we know Him, but because we cannot worship Him well—and perhaps because the Europeans do not sell people, for these reasons we were glad.

Two Bird Songs of the Pokomo Women

Translated from the Swahili by Dr. Alice Werner, who took them down from Isaya Zakariya of Ngao. Ndarama, the sister of Isaya, composed 'The Osprey' on an occasion when she was going down to the river to draw water when she saw a fish-eagle sitting on a tree.

THE OSPREY

Hear him calling there on the tree,
Flapping his wings and shaking his head!
A brave and comely bird is he
With his shining plumes so bright to see.
As I went down to the river-bed
Bearing my water-jar on my head
I saw him on the kurubo tree.

THE PLOVER

Plover, my lover, how lightly you hover
The water over!
Gracefully darting and skimming, what time the rivers
are brimming.
Oh! lovely, lovely bird—bright eyes and crested head!
All night I lie awake till the dawn comes up red,
Thinking of your white wings, beloved, O Plover!

unwillingness of the slaves to confess that they were so. This was partly from a vague fear of people they knew nothing about, but mainly because the Arabs used to tell them that all Europeans were cannibals, and only caught slaves in order to fatten and eat them.

The Cunning of Suud

MBARAK ALI HINAWY

Editor's note: The Mazrui chieftain, Sheikh Mbaruk bin Rashid bin Salim el-Mazrui, has rebelled against the Sultan of Zanzibar, Seyyid Barghash, and has made so many daring raids along the coast of the mainland, that Muhammad bin Abdallah, known as Al-Akida, the Sultan's acting Wali in Mombasa, determines to make a secret punitive expedition. He has guards posted at all the ferries linking Mombasa with the mainland to prevent news of his plans from leaking out or word being carried to Sheikh Mbaruk. Sheikh Mbaruk's sympathisers in Mombasa, however, devise a clever plan to warn him of his danger.

THERE were at that time two dancing-parties in Mombasa, who called themselves the Mbura and the Mrani. They staged their performances every night, and, to the accompaniment of drums, songs were sung, some of them composed especially for the occasion but others extemporized by the performers. The impromptu composition of such songs has always been regarded as a skilled accomplishment of Swahili *washairi*,[1] as indeed it is. To gain acceptance, much more popularity, such songs must hit off some topical theme ; they must follow the type of the *ngoma*,[2] and be marked by the use of graceful and melodious phraseology ; and they must, of course, conform to the acknowledged rules of composition and be perfect in rhyme and measure.

One night, while Al-Akida was immersed in his secret plans for the capture of Sheikh Mbaruk, and while his guards maintained careful watch upon Mombasa's water-ways, there appeared at one of the dances in the town a man whose skill in versification was equalled only by his anxiety for his friend, the Mazrui chieftain. He was none other than Sheikh Suud bin Said al-Maamiry, the renowned and accomplished Swahili poet, one of Sheikh Mbaruk's staunchest friends, and an inveterate enemy of Al-Akida. He was determined to let Sheikh Mbaruk know of the secret preparations for his capture, and to circumvent Al-Akida's schemes for preventing the transmission of the news across the ferries.

[1] poets.　　　　　　　　　　　　[2] dance.

His plan was as simple as it was ingenious. He would warn his friend through the medium of songs. As Suud well knew, verses which caught the popular fancy travelled quickly to the neighbouring villages on the lips of those whose work took them afield on the following day. Accordingly, Suud took his place one night at a Mbura-dance and composed some verses which, coming from a poet so well known to them, were taken up by the throng and sung with enthusiasm. In the excitement of the dance and the thrill of singing no one paid particular attention to the words, which ostensibly were just amusing skits on the *wateje* or initiates of the witchdoctors, and on the popular dance known as the *tari la ndia*. But, like a great many similar Swahili compositions, Suud's verses bore a hidden meaning, which had nothing at all to do with the witchdoctors or the *tari la ndia!* So it came about that within a day or two the crews of the dhows putting in at Gasi, and men and women crossing the ferries to the mainland from the bazaars of Mombasa, were singing the words of Mombasa's latest song-hit:

'The throngs of wizard's followers have donned their beaded cords,
So wait ye now the coming of these strange-garbed demon hordes.
O wizard, be prepared for those who leap high on the swards!

With naked sword and dagger the Wakilindini dance,
And he who is a stranger had best stand aside and glance.
Know well, Mbura-dancers, lest ye meet with swift mischance.

Mbura-dancer, think not 'tis some outworn dance of old,
Danced by unruly men who, dancing, dance it overbold.
But stand ye in the open; let your own brave worth be told.'

Such was the simple refrain of the verses as Sheikh Mbaruk and his followers heard them at Gasi a few hours later, as a catchy popular song of topical skits upon the Mbura-dancers. But Sheikh Mbaruk was a shrewd and clever leader. He quickly divined Suud's hidden message and left Gasi for his stronghold at Mwele Hill, where he set to work in all haste to barricade himself in and strengthen his defences.

To him the message had been clear enough. The wizard was Al-Akida; his *wateje* were his men-at-arms; the *pagaro*, pieces of twig strung together and worn across the shoulders by the witchdoctors' folk, were the bandoliers of Al-Akida's soldiery. Furthermore, if the Wakilindini, the folk of Mombasa, were armed with their swords and daggers, it was not for the stranger (Al-Akida) to intervene; so let not Mbura (Sheikh Mbaruk) be taken unawares.

Finally, let Mbaruk not think that this attack was to be any half-hearted attempt like the previous ones, or that Al-Akida's soldiery were a fainthearted following; for they were the *Wangaro*, literally, dancers wearing their loincloths tucked high above their knees, or in other words, the Hadhramaut Arabs of Al-Akida's army, whose custom it was to wear their loincloths above their knees.

Thus the song had a very different meaning for Sheikh Mbaruk from that of the simple verses which amused the Mbura-dancers enjoying their evening's pleasure at Mombasa.

As we have said, Mbaruk left Gasi and entrenched himself at Mwele: but the warning, welcome as it was, had given him insufficient time to resist Al-Akida's attack successfully.

Finding that he had gone from Gasi, Al-Akida's troops followed him to Mwele, and there engaged his forces so hotly that he was compelled to make a hasty retreat.

Mwele Hill was captured.

The Gentlemen of the Jungle

A Gikuyu [1] Tale

Told by

JOMO KENYATTA

Introducing the tale, Jomo Kenyatta says 'The relation between the Gikuyu and the Europeans can well be illustrated by this Gikuyu story.'

ONCE upon a time an elephant made a friendship with a man. One day a heavy thunderstorm broke out, the elephant went to his friend, who had a little hut at the edge of the forest, and said to him: 'My dear good man, will you please let me put my trunk inside your hut to keep it out of this torrential rain?' The man, seeing what situation his friend was in, replied: 'My dear good elephant, my hut is very small, but there is room for your trunk

[1] More usually Kikuyu.

and myself. Please put your trunk in gently.' The elephant thanked his friend, saying : 'You have done me a good deed and one day I shall return your kindness.' But what followed? As soon as the elephant put his trunk inside the hut, slowly he pushed his head inside, and finally flung the man out in the rain, and then lay down comfortably inside his friend's hut, saying : 'My dear good friend, your skin is harder than mine, and as there is not enough room for both of us, you can afford to remain in the rain while I am protecting my delicate skin from the hailstorm.'

The man, seeing what his friend had done to him, started to grumble; the animals in the nearby forest heard the noise and came to see what was the matter. All stood around listening to the heated argument between the man and his friend the elephant. In this turmoil the lion came along roaring, and said in a loud voice : 'Don't you all know that I am the King of the Jungle! How dare anyone disturb the peace of my kingdom?' On hearing this the elephant, who was one of the high ministers in the jungle kingdom, replied in a soothing voice, and said : 'My lord, there is no disturbance of the peace in your kingdom. I have only been having a little discussion with my friend here as to the possession of this little hut which your lordship sees me occupying.' The lion, who wanted to have 'peace and tranquillity' in his kingdom, replied in a noble voice, saying : 'I command my ministers to appoint a Commission of Enquiry to go thoroughly into this matter and report accordingly.' He then turned to the man and said : 'You have done well by establishing friendship with my people, especially with the elephant, who is one of my honourable ministers of state. Do not grumble any more, your hut is not lost to you. Wait until the sitting of my Imperial Commission, and there you will be given plenty of opportunity to state your case. I am sure that you will be pleased with the findings of the Commission.' The man was very pleased by these sweet words from the King of the Jungle, and innocently waited for his opportunity, in the belief that naturally the hut would be returned to him.

The elephant, obeying the command of his master, got busy with other ministers to appoint the Commission of Enquiry. The following elders of the jungle were appointed to sit in the Commission : (1) Mr. Rhinoceros; (2) Mr. Buffalo ; (3) Mr. Alligator ; (4) The Rt. Hon. Mr. Fox to act as chairman ; and (5) Mr. Leopard to act as Secretary to the Commission. On seeing the personnel, the man protested and asked if it was not necessary to include in this Commission a member from his side. But he was told that it was impossible, since no one from his side was well enough educated to understand the intricacy of jungle law. Further, that there was nothing to fear, for the members of the Commission were all men of repute for their impartiality in justice, and as they were gentlemen chosen by God to look after the interests of races less adequately endowed with teeth and claws, he might rest assured that they would investigate the matter with the greatest care and report impartially.

The Commission sat to take the evidence. The Rt. Hon. Mr. Elephant was first called. He came along with a superior air, brushing his tusks with a sapling which Mrs. Elephant had provided, and in an authoritative voice said : 'Gentlemen of the Jungle, there is no need for me to waste your valuable time in relating a story which I am sure you all know. I have always regarded it as my duty to protect the interests of my friends, and this appears to have caused the misunderstanding between myself and my friend here. He invited me to save his hut from being blown away by a hurricane. As the hurricane had gained access owing to the unoccupied space in the hut, I considered it necessary, in my friend's own interests, to turn the undeveloped space to a more economic use by sitting in it myself ; a duty which any of you would undoubtedly have performed with equal readiness in similar circumstances.'

After hearing the Rt. Hon. Mr. Elephant's conclusive evidence, the Commission called Mr. Hyena and other elders of the jungle, who all supported what Mr. Elephant had said. They then called the man, who began to give his own account of the dispute. But the Commission cut him short, saying : 'My good man, please confine yourself to relevant issues. We have already heard the circumstances from various unbiased sources ; all we wish you to tell us is whether the undeveloped space in your hut was occupied by anyone else before Mr. Elephant assumed his position?' The man began to say : 'No, but—' But at this point the Commission declared that they had heard sufficient evidence from both sides and retired to consider their decision. After enjoying a delicious meal at the expense of the Rt. Hon. Mr. Elephant, they reached their verdict, called the man, and declared as follows : 'In our opinion this dispute has arisen through a regrettable misunderstanding due to the backwardness of your ideas. We consider that Mr. Elephant has fulfilled his sacred duty of protecting your interests. As it is clearly for your good that the space should be put to its most economic use, and as you yourself have not yet reached the stage of expansion which would enable you to fill it, we consider it necessary to arrange a compromise to suit both parties. Mr. Elephant shall continue his occupation of your hut, but we give you permission to look for a site where you can build another hut more suited to your needs, and we will see that you are well protected.'

The man, having no alternative, and fearing that his refusal might expose him to the teeth and claws of members of the Commission, did as they suggested. But no sooner had he built another hut than Mr. Rhinoceros charged in with his horn lowered and ordered the man to quit. A Royal Commission was again appointed to look into the matter, and the same finding was given. This procedure was repeated until Mr. Buffalo, Mr. Leopard, Mr. Hyena and the rest were all accommodated with new huts. Then the man decided that he must adopt an effective method of protection, since Commissions of Enquiry did not seem to be of any use to him. He sat down and said : '*Ng'enda thi ndagaga motegi*,' which literally means 'there is nothing that treads on the earth that cannot be trapped,' or in other words, you can fool people for a time, but not for ever.

Early one morning, when the huts already occupied by the jungle lords were all beginning to decay and fall to pieces, he went out and built a bigger and better hut a little distance away. No sooner had Mr. Rhinoceros seen it than he came rushing in, only to find that Mr. Elephant was already inside, sound asleep. Mr. Leopard next came in at the window, Mr. Lion, Mr. Fox and Mr. Buffalo entered the doors, while Mr. Hyena howled for a place in the shade and Mr. Alligator basked on the roof. Presently they all began disputing about their rights of penetration, and from disputing they came to fighting, and while they were all embroiled together the man set the hut on fire and burnt it to the ground, jungle lords and all. Then he went home, saying : 'Peace is costly, but it's worth the expense,' and lived happily ever after.

'Much silence has a mighty noise.' [1]

[1] A Swahili saying.

Central Africa

Stanley Meets Mutesa

JAMES D. RUBADIRI

Such a time of it they had;
The heat of the day
The chill of the night
And the mosquitoes that followed.
Such was the time and
They bound for a kingdom.

The thin weary line of carriers
With tattered dirty rags to cover their backs;
The battered bulky chests
That kept on falling off their shaven heads.
Their tempers high and hot
The sun fierce and scorching
With it rose their spirits
With its fall their hopes
As each day sweated their bodies dry and
Flies clung in clumps on their sweat-scented backs.
Such was the march
And the hot season just breaking.

Each day a weary pony dropped,
Left for the vultures on the plains;
Each afternoon a human skeleton collapsed,
Left for the Masai on the plains;
But the march trudged on
Its Khaki leader in front
He the spirit that inspired.
He the light of hope.

Then came the afternoon of a hungry march,
A hot and hungry march it was;
The Nile and the Nyanza
Lay like two twins

Azure across the green countryside.
The march leapt on chaunting
Like young gazelles to a water hole.
Hearts beat faster
Loads felt lighter
As the cool water lapt their sore soft feet.
No more the dread of hungry hyenas
But only tales of valour when
At Mutesa's court fires are lit.
No more the burning heat of the day
But song, laughter and dance.

The village looks on behind banana groves,
Children peer behind reed fences.
Such was the welcome
No singing women to chaunt a welcome
Or drums to greet the white ambassador;
Only a few silent nods from aged faces
And one rumbling drum roll
To summon Mutesa's court to parley
For the country was not sure.

The gate of reeds is flung open,
There is silence
But only a moment's silence—
A silence of assessment.
The tall black king steps forward,
He towers over the thin bearded white man
Then grabbing his lean white hand
Manages to whisper
'Mtu mweupe karibu'
White man you are welcome.
The gate of polished reed closes behind them
And the west is let in.

The 'Angola'

OSCAR RIBAS

Translated from the Portuguese by Dr. Mora de Vasconcelos
and adapted by Peggy Rutherfoord

IT was a halcyon day in March. The afternoon sky was hazy. The sun was dying in a soft agony of colour. A light breeze was blowing. It was a scene of nostalgic nuances.

Lisbon crackled on the quay. There, people were dressed, some elegantly, some roughly, but all were consumed by the same flame; and like sparks leaping from the fire, the emotions burst from the heart; there were mouths that demanded; mouths that kissed; eyes that promised; eyes that wept; hands that quivered and clung to each other without restraint; breasts that throbbed in tender embraces; souls torn asunder in an anguish of weeping, and already each one was laying on the pedestal of their love, the first offerings of their longing.

The 'Angola' moved out ponderously. Sirens sounded. Then, as if shocked into activity by her departure, hundreds of waving handkerchiefs seconded the great voice of the heart, 'Farewell! Farewell!'

Like glow-worms in the fastness of night doubt stabbed the fog of sadness. Alas, who knows whether they will come back? How many mothers will be bereft of their sons, how many wives without their husbands? How much joy, how much sorrow, will the separation bring? Will they be happy in those lands of fever? Will they find work there, riches and dignity? God would surely help them in their desires?

Another siren is heard. The air weeps; love weeps within the heart. Handkerchiefs flutter more anxiously still, waving 'Farewell! Farewell!' Now, those who remain hold council with themselves. Grief is swallowed into the deep distance.

In this last farewell, the boat shivers mournfully. The melancholy deepens and grows cold. That sadness, alas, suggests the last throes of death.

And, followed by the seagulls—messengers of those who are left behind—there they go in their floating world, exchanging Portugal for those far-off lands. Will it be for ever? Nobody can tell. Life frames a question which submerges the soul.

Sky and sea are all that remain now from the gulf of past days.

Escapade in Ruanda

J. SAVERIO NAIGIZIKI

Translated from the French by Dorothy Blair

🪷

N I N E T E E N hundred and forty-five. The saddest year of my waning youth. The most dizzy turning point perhaps of my life, and certainly the most difficult of my past existence.

Here I am, a man of doubtful morals, a salesman in Nyanza.

Time and again I have balanced the money entrusted to me, and still it shows a merciless deficit, whose size terrifies me, a hole that I have dug myself, out of weakness, to oblige my friends, but which no friend up to date is willing to help me fill! Alas! all my own efforts only result in digging it even deeper.

I have written to inform Father Norsen. But the visit which he paid me, while paternal and sympathetic, hurt me.

He asks me what means I have at my disposal to repay the sums which are missing from my till. I hesitate to tell him openly that I was counting on him. He senses this and confesses that for some time he has not had a penny in his purse. Then I myself confess, with much reticence and embarrassment, that I have already thought of a little business arrangement to settle things; it is somewhat shady, like all business arrangements, but, I told him, the ends I have in view are innocent. He does not understand, and without insisting he wishes me better luck and goes. He can do nothing. He is overwhelmed.

Leaning sadly on the counter, I watch the good Father leave amidst a crowd of children who ply him with questions. He answers evasively, without seeing them, and walks away heavily, in spite of his youth, his hands behind his back, his head bent forward, under the weight of his thoughts.

It is Tuesday, about ten o'clock. There is not much business in the market on weekdays. I neglect the few customers who only ask for worthless articles. My assistant manages as best he can. At last they go away without buying anything. They always come in like this when the sun is hot, begging or stealing something in the shops.

Kambeja, my oil-seller, who is used to teasing me, notices my uneasiness. This time she comes wheedling like a little spoilt puppy that wants to be stroked, puts her little lips against my cheek, and in a childish prattle, which she emphasizes with an adorable smile, she invites me to her house this evening.

'You shall have all that you are hungry for, all that you are thirsty for, the thousand and one things that you wish for!'

That woman has ways all her own of bending my will! Without a word I gaze at her with a look of assent. Certain of her success, she leaves me, going off with a satisfied air, smoothing her little waist, throwing back her head and showing the shining ivory of her teeth.

I should like to go home for a drink. But I am afraid of Suzanne's searching eye. My memory, which will let me forget nothing, brings back yesterday's scene. I see Suzanne—my wife before men, if not before God—lashed by furious jealousy, spitting in my face, tearing her hair, cursing the oil-seller.

What is the good of facing this fury now, before whom I am always in the wrong . . . as before my conscience?

But, heavens above! there she is coming through the door towards me. Her stirring beauty, usually magnetic and fascinating, but now as imposing as the façade of a court of justice, rigid as a fate that must be suffered, terrifies and crushes me.

Where can I flee? Where can I not flee? Her bitter gaze seeks and attacks mine violently. I feel it and bear it weakly.

Does she come, severe as yesterday, to humiliate me before this rabble of spiteful ne'er-do-wells, who drag their eternal sloth about shop entrances? And these street-loafers who pop in and out to see and hear? And this smart group of up-to-date women who sell their flesh to male caprices, and who hawk corruption in the cities and bankruptcy in business. How ashamed I shall be!

She comes up towards me :

'It is almost mid-day,' she says, between her teeth ; 'you can close the shop. Then go out by the inside door ; I want to talk to you.'

I should like to resist her. But her grand-lady manner flusters me.

In the room, where Suzanne has preceded me, the table is already laid. A savoury-smelling chicken, already carved, swims in a golden sauce on the enamel of a deep plate. Beside it, a dish containing a white tapioca loaf, a bottle of *pombe* and two clean glasses.

'Sit down,' she says, 'eat and drink. You need it.'

While I empty the glass, she continues, first conciliating, then ironical :

'For the past week you have been changing from hour to hour. You are no longer yourself. I scarcely recognize you. You eat without appetite in spite of the variety of the food ; you neglect me. Forget yesterday evening as I have forgotten it myself. It is the fault of that she-devil of a salesgirl. If I was strong enough to supplant in your heart your legitimate wife, no other woman, except your wife, you understand, no other thieving woman has the right to take away that place from me. Only your wife has the right to occupy your heart, and I alone after her. I'll settle the salesgirl, as I have a right to, and not her alone, but Athanasia, Jozefa and all the feminine rabble of Nyanza.'

'Calm yourself, Suzanne. You know perfectly well that I love you. I have told you so a hundred times. Do not scold your man. I do love you. Do you want me to tell you all the time?'

'It is not enough to say so, you must prove it : prove it by acts of love. Are your games of hide-and-seek with the salesgirl proofs of love towards me? Rather agree that they are quite unequivocal marks of treachery, which make me doubt your love and despair of your heart. I don't want your love shared with all women. You must give it all to me. And if nowadays I am nasty to you, it is my way, dearest, of showing you my love.'

'Then be less cruel, Suzanne. Just give me till this evening. Then we shall be more at ease. I will tell you all my troubles, my misfortunes. I will pour out my whole love to you. Suzanne, I give you the choice : love me for always, or leave me for ever.'

'You men, perhaps you can see further than women, but you cannot see as deeply. You reason, we feel. You promise, we give. At any rate, let it be as you say. I will wait for you at the time you say, as one waits for one's man, and I will be prepared to welcome you. I love you too much, Justin, to think of ever hating you. And my greatest worry here, ever since I have been yours, would be to lose you. But be sure that you give yourself without reserve, that you tell everything unrestrictedly. If you have troubles, I shall understand them. But, heavens above, eat the food prepared for you. You are growing terribly thin. And I am ashamed to see you together with your pals. Sit yourself down, here, beside me, and spare me the trouble of having cooked all this for your boys.'

Under her light-hearted glance, which gaily meets mine, I sit down at her left, on the fragrant bed, amidst the lingering perfume of nights of love.

And I attack the meal with the best will in the world. But I have difficulty in finishing the chicken and in polishing off three quarters of my bread.

'That's right,' says Suzanne. 'I thank you, and now I am satisfied. At this rate, it won't be long before we make peace.'

'Yes, I shall keep my word, and in future I shall be kind and light-hearted, since you are the first to lay down arms.'

And as I get up to go, she stops me :

'Don't go off so quickly. You know your boy is back from Astrida. Your chief has gone to Urundi for the stock-taking. He will no doubt be back on Monday or Tuesday, next week. It seems that your agents in Astrida have done a miserable job. So the stock-taking will soon be here. . . . Think in advance of what you are going to do.'

'Don't worry. I have calculated everything, and foreseen everything. I don't want to see my boy immediately. For the moment I have an appointment with Mr. Miwa's clerk. I must hurry off there and I'll be back at two o'clock. Thank you for deciding to make peace and for giving me back my appetite. Above all, forget our fall-out of yesterday, and remember that in my eyes there's no woman can equal you.'

Standing before the enormous mass of the shop, I gaze at the emptying market. Odd-job men, beggars for the most part, are sweeping up, and go to throw away the scraps, for a penny, for a bone, for a bit of meat. Poor folk !

At the Fathers' the bell gravely, fervently strikes twelve. In the Judicial Territory, three proud bugle-notes announce the closing of offices, and hunger and thirst in people's bellies.

Yonder, in the street at the other end of the market, some prisoners stagger, like a human herd stampeding, in faded jerseys like old sacks, urged on by a soldier in a hurry to eat. These poor prisoners, dead to themselves, go joylessly to taste of a meagre repast and slender repose. And yet, although recognized as guilty, they are surely not the worst of men !

I feel a need to go up to the church. Now Jesus, the dispenser of full pardon, is alone. He will be pleased with my visit at this solitary hour.

I walk past the firms of Costa, Antonio, Petron, Marangos, turn my back on Rahematali and Vakiris, and make my way to the Mission, leaving behind me the Law Courts and the Judicial Territory.

Before the colossal statue of the Christ-King, beneath His hand dispensing blessings, I am seized with a vague hope. With this salutary impression in my heart, I hurry into the Holy Place, deserted at this hour when every man is thinking of himself. I feel the eyes of Jesus covering me. And my supplications arise, arise ever higher, arise in serried ranks, urgent, tear-laden.

'How calm and cool it is in your prison, oh, my God! Remember me, Lord, and the little good that I have done. Do not abandon me to the mercy of my fate.

'You know that I did not steal that vile money.

'I was very wrong to use and perhaps to lose for ever what did not belong to me. But it was to save good folk who were threatened with prison and disgrace. The till was full to overflowing with money and my heart with goodness. I opened both, spontaneously, irresistibly. Nuco's till and my own heart! . . .

'I thought I had to do it. And this complete consciousness of the good I did, perhaps erroneously, excuses my conduct.

'Perhaps in ten days' time I shall be going to increase the crowd of convicts, of whom I saw a sample just now. It is probable, more than possible even, unless a miracle happens.

'Do not let it happen, oh Lord! Rather perform the miracle which alone can save me!

'You know my fits of anger and my obstinacy. You know that all in me is madness. All my actions, dictated by passion, are always carried to the extreme, to rashness. Spare the Government, the Public Power, the trouble of having to do violence to my dull wits, my crazed heart, to my clear conscience. For my tempestuous nature encloses, like the universe, every contrast. You will spare me, too, the pain of suffering in prison the miniature death of every day; the calculated diminution of my personality; the progressive dismemberment, cruelly refined and consciously inflicted on the weakness of mankind by the strength of mankind.

'And to suffer all these atrocities with the gibes, the spitting, the lash, all the hate-inspired blackguardry of the soldiers.

'Oh Lord, keep these afflictions far from me, however well-deserved they may be.

'Treat me, Lord, according to your divine and paternal justice, you who can read into the heart, and know the causes of our actions better than we do ourselves, you alone, in whom infinite justice does not exclude extreme goodness. Let it not enter into your plans to deliver me over to men nor to their tortuous judgments.

'I came into this church, urged on by you, summoned by you.

'Faith told me that I must still hope, in spite of everything. Be always there at my side, to dictate to me your will, to pardon my faults, to spare my poor security, to accompany my inevitable flight.

'For indeed I shall flee. But when? But how? Whatever the

manner, I prefer the hardships of flight to the horrors of prison.

'Africa is vast. I shall run with unfettered limbs, I shall die of exhaustion. And thus I shall be able to break free from Suzanne and live, an exile, but a free exile, according to your laws.

'Nevertheless, oh Lord, I shall await your blessing and the hour of your miracles.'

Down in the choir, the Fathers have arrived, reciting the Psalm of the Penitents in a monotone, and have left again, casting a curious glance in my direction. One alone among them knows the secret of my sorrows. And he no doubt has prayed for me. May God give ear to his prayers and to mine.

Soon after I left, my heart lighter. And with my pipe between my lips, I had the courage to hum a tune.

Madagascar

The Flute-Players

JEAN-JOSEPH RABÉARIVELO

Translated from the French by Dorothy Blair

Your flute,
    you fashioned from the shin of a mighty bull
    and you polished it on the arid hillsides
    scourged by the sun;
    his flute,
    he fashioned from a quivering reed in the breeze
    and he pierced it at the brink of running waters
    drunk with the dreams of the moon.

You play your flutes together in the depths of the evening,
    as if to hold back the spherical canoe
    which capsizes at the banks of the heavens;
    as if to deliver it
    from its fate:
    but your plaintive songs
    are they heard by the gods of the winds,
    of the earth and of the forest,
    and of the sand?

Your flute
    draws out a note charged with the stamp of a raging bull
    which runs to the waste-lands
    and returns at a run,
    scorched by thirst and hunger,
    but felled with fatigue
    at the foot of a tree that is shadeless,
    fruitless, leafless.
    His flute
    is like a pliant reed
    bending 'neath the weight of a bird of passage—
    not a bird caught by a child
    with ruffled feathers,
    but a bird far from his own kin

watching his shadow, to seek consolation,
on the running water.

Your flute
and his—
mourn for their origins
in the songs of your sorrows.

The Water-Seeker

FLAVIEN RANAIVO

Translated from the French by Dorothy Blair

A Dove is she
who goes down
the rocky path
sliding like
a capricious pebble
on the steep slope
towards the spring.

The water-seeker.

She descends
with clumsy care,
catching
time and again
with one hand
on the aloe leaves
smooth and pointed,
with the other
she holds the earthen pitcher
—of the country earth—
Scarcely sure
those naked
feet
of the girl of Imerina.
What can she be dreaming
beneath her thick *lamba*

which yet moulds
breasts half guessed, sharp
smooth and pointed?
—'What can you be dreaming
Amber-skinned-one
Almond-eyed-one?'—
What can she be thinking
she-who-has-never-known
nor joy nor sorrow
nor love nor hate . . .
Alluring yet
those lying
lips :
so smooth and pointed?
A breath,
the breath of a breeze
has so soon ruffled
her black hair.
What can she be dreaming
this soul-less body
which ruffles
the soul of the poet?
Sweet
deceit.

The Lyre with Seven Strings

JACQUES RABÉMANANJARA

Translated from the French by Dorothy Blair

You will follow me, pale Sister,
Chosen before the dawn of the world!
Bride when the earth was still without form and void
Sole reason of the Creation! Power of my destiny!

You will come.
Vain
Will be the cries of your blood, the grumbling pride of
    your race.

You will follow me.
March of love! Flight of the dove!
O Freshness of the first morning!

Your brothers
Have grown deaf,
insensible even to the smell of powder, to the fury of
the thunder.

Harder
than granite their hearts drunk with carnage and death.

The sweetness of your message, my sister,
has only moved the myriad ranks
of the stars,
only moved my primitive soul,
mirror and sole reflection of your lot.

They have understood nothing
in the tumult of the massacre, in the glowing of the
fires.
Folly
has galloped
whinneying
from the entrails of the abyss to the rent summit of
space and sky.

Yet from the four points of the horizon
arise
the sounds of a trumpet and the curves of your high
melodies,
O Peace!
Daughter of the dolorous Earth!
Image of the Loved-one, honey of spring on the blue
banks of Assoussiel.

You will come, pale Sister, to the country of dreams, to the banks
of royal springs.
White, white the orchid at the peak of the Hill of Alassour!
The paths are aglow with peonies under the fires of immemorial
colours.
And the breeze from the South troubles the virginal pool with the
whispered secrets of love.

West Africa

O Lamb give me my Salt

This poem, written several centuries ago in Ibo, a
language of Nigeria, was translated by D. C. Osadebay

O Lamb give me my salt,
Salt the market folks gave me;
The market folk ate my fruits,
Fruits the fruit picker gave me;
The farmer broke my hoe,
Hoe the smith gave me;
The smith ate my yam,
Yam an old woman gave me;
The old woman ate my bird,
The bird my trap gave me,
My faithful, useful trap.

The Stolen Jacket

CAMARA LAYE

Translated from the French by Dorothy Blair

⚜

Translator's note: Clarence, a white man, destitute in a black kingdom, has given his jacket to the keeper of a sordid hostelry in exchange for his board and lodging, and now leaves, accompanied by a beggar and two youths.

A S they left the lodging-house, Clarence was more than a little surprised to find the city in a state of feverish activity. A little while before, as they came down from the parade ground, it had been sleeping and deserted, sleeping logically enough, since night had already fallen, but unaccountably deserted. He found it now over-flowing with life and noise, a prey to tumult, the tumult of the street, but of what a street; the most restless, the most swarming of streets : the African street!

Everywhere the drums were rumbling, rolling, imparting their quivering to the reeds, to the bamboo fences, to the mud-walls, even to the earth and to the sky, and above all to the crowd, which moved to its rhythm and which, even at a standstill, continued to sway and shouted, and clapped and uttered cries on every note from grave to shrill, but particularly, most violently, the shrill notes : hoarse cries of the men, piercing cries of the women, especially the women; women who thrust themselves forward, boldly forward, their breasts uncovered, and rushed and hurled themselves into the dance, surrendering themselves nakedly to a trepidation and a fury which should by rights have soon left them panting, but which, on the other hand, threw them into an ever greater, ever more consuming passion, and finally cast them into such a frenzy as transformed the crossroads with their blazing fires into the rendezvous of a witches' sabbath.

As they prepared to break through the crowd they unexpectedly found themselves surrounded by a detachment of the royal guards. The guards were staring at them, without a word, without moving; they were all of the same build as the beggar, but unlike him were youthful and strong; they stood erect, pressed close shoulder to shoulder; they were like a wall; and above this wall, only a little of the night could be seen, a little patch of night seen through a skylight.

'What do these people want?' asked Clarence. 'Why are they shutting us in as in a prison?'

'How do I know?' retorted the beggar.

'Then why don't you drive them away,' said Clarence.

But scarcely had he uttered these words than he saw the Negro lodging-house keeper slip through into the prison.

'At last I've got you!' shouted the landlord, grabbing Clarence by the scruff of his neck.

'Hands off!' said the beggar severely.

'Oh, no!' screamed the landlord. 'This time I've the law on my side; and beggar you may be, but you don't impress me any more. I want my jacket. I won't take my hands off till the white man has given me back my jacket.'

'But I've given it to you already!' said Clarence. 'I gave it you against my will, but I did give it you.'

'And you took it back again!' shouted the landlord.

'Are you mad?' said Clarence. 'I have never seen you again since I gave it to you.'

No sooner had he finished the sentence than the guards who surrounded them began to laugh, bending double as if they had heard the funniest thing on earth. 'What's got hold of them?' Clarence wondered. But they were doubtless a bit drunk. People of their sort must have had repeated conversations with the gourds hung on the trees. They were obviously drunk.

'I am not joking,' Clarence said firmly.

But they began to laugh and sway again, worse than ever.

'Come on, give him back his jacket,' said one of the guards who wore a rope girdle over his tunic. 'Return it and we won't say anything more about it.'

'How can I return it to him?' said Clarence. 'I have already given it to him.'

'Well, give it to him again, if you like it better that way,' said the guard with the rope. 'I'm not a stickler for language; and I don't want to get you into trouble.'

'What is this joke?' shouted Clarence. 'I don't think it at all funny.' He turned towards the beggar and saw him drinking peacefully, as if what was happening was no concern of his.

'Why don't you say something?' said Clarence.

'What do you want me to say?' said the beggar. 'There is obviously a mistake. But how are you going to prove it?'

'Can't you swear that you have never left my side?'

'I swear it,' said the beggar solemnly.

'Have you decided to return the jacket to the landlord?' said the guard with the rope to Clarence.

'For the last time, I tell you that I have given it to him, and I haven't got it any more,' said Clarence. 'It is impossible to be more explicit.'

'What a pity!' said the guard. 'And God knows that I didn't want to use force, but . . . Guards, seize him! and the beggar, too!'

Immediately the guards seized Clarence's hands and those of the beggar. 'Now follow me to the judge,' said the guard with the rope. 'And don't try to escape; it will only make things worse for you.'

The little group formed a procession. The crowd that had massed behind the guards opened their ranks. Clarence advanced between two walls of inquisitive faces. The rumour rapidly spread that he had been arrested for theft. Clarence felt terribly embarrassed. His confusion suddenly increased when he perceived, near one of the fires, a group of white men who had come to see the dancers. He would like to have spoken to them, but could not find the right words. The money that he owed them was hardly a recommendation. He tried to make himself small, hoping to pass unnoticed, but he did not succeed: the white men had immediately located him.

'My word, they're arresting him!' said one.

'It looks like it,' said another.

'Bah! It's all finishing as it should have begun,' said a third with a shrug of his shoulders. 'The first glance told me that he was a drifter. As for the second glance; you know as much about it as I do.'

They laughed long and derisively, as if to invite others to join in their sneers. Clarence felt a furious desire to tell them that it was all a mistake, and that the misunderstanding would certainly be cleared up in front of the judge: but it did not take him long to realize that the best explanation would not help him: these men had made up their minds! He made himself small again, bending his head nearer to the ground.

'See how he hangs his head,' said one of the white men. 'Would he hang it so low if he were not guilty? No one will make me admit that this fellow isn't guilty.'

Clarence was tempted to raise his head, but what was the use? Was not everything against him? If he had gone by with his head raised high, they would have said that he was shameless, or that he was compromising the prestige of the white man, or something or other which would have been to his disadvantage, for it is not one's actions that count, but the interpretation that is put on them.

'What can I do?' Clarence thought. 'Everything turns against me. . . . Perhaps I am unwise—I am certainly unwise—but other people are too, others are more so than me.'

At this point his thoughts were interrupted by his being suddenly pushed into a corridor.

The corridor was narrow, and as winding as the alleyways of the town, but it was completely silent and on each side innumerable doors opened on to it. The doors, naturally enough, all remained obstinately shut, except the last one, right at the end of the corridor. This last door opened as if of its own accord in front of the little group; and Clarence saw himself to be in a huge room, the biggest he had seen since he landed. At the end of the room was a man squatting on a table and telling his beads. This man stared at Clarence for some minutes.

'So this is the guilty party,' he said at last.

'I am not guilty!' cried Clarence.

The man raised his hand.

'Everybody who comes here says that. You have no idea how tired I am of hearing it! . . . The main thing is that you are here, and that they wasted no time in catching you. . . . And who's this man?' he asked, pointing to the beggar.

'His accomplice,' said the landlord.

'I did not ask you,' said the man. 'You will speak when you're spoken to. And nothing—nothing, you understand?—proves yet that you will be spoken to. I shall speak to you only in so far as I see any necessity. . . . Come now, who is he?' he asked again.

He seemed impatient; his finger remained pointing at the beggar.

'It's the beggar who was with the white man,' said the guard with the rope. 'I thought I'd better bring him along.'

'You did well,' said the man. 'He will be a witness for the prosecution.'

'I say . . .' said Clarence.

'Address me as Your Honour, the Chief Magistrate,' said the judge.

'Your Honour, the Chief Magistrate,' said Clarence, 'this man, who is a beggar, has not left me all evening. He will tell you that I gave my jacket to the landlord, in payment for the time I spent in his inn, and that I have never for one moment taken the jacket back.'

'Oh, no!' said the judge. 'Your method is no use. This man,' pointing to the beggar, 'is the witness for the prosecution. You can't turn him into a witness for the defence: it would be contrary to the law. . . . Find another argument.'

'But what can I find?' said Clarence.

'The jacket, my friend, the jacket!' said the judge. 'That's all you are asked for.'

'The landlord has got it,' said Clarence.

'Look here!' said the judge. 'Think before you speak. Why would the landlord have run after you if you hadn't taken the jacket back? . . . A child could understand that.'

'I don't know!' replied Clarence. 'Who says that this man isn't accusing me out of pure malice?'

'We must go into that,' said the judge.

He seemed to think for a moment, his beads slipping rapidly through his fingers.

'I have thought it over,' he said a minute later. 'Are you in the habit of telling lies?'

'I never lie!' said Clarence.

'Excuse me, Your Honour, the Chief Magistrate,' said the guard with the rope. 'When I charged him, the white man claimed that he had not seen the landlord since he had left the inn. Now, he made that statement at the very moment when the landlord was standing in front of him. And so we all began to laugh.'

'That's not very good evidence in favour of your truthfulness,' said the judge to Clarence.

'They misunderstood,' said Clarence. 'I said . . . .'

'Don't forget that the guards are under oath,' said the judge. 'They are not permitted to lie in my presence, even if, when off duty, they were the most arrant liars on earth. Did you say anything different from what the chief guard has just repeated?'

'The chief guard reproduced my words exactly, only he put a wrong interpretation upon them.'

'Good, good!' said the judge. 'Don't let us argue for a quarter of an hour about interpretations : everything in good time ; this business is sufficiently complicated as it is. . . . So you admit that the chief guard has faithfully reproduced your words. That's an argument in your favour, at least in favour of your truthfulness, but as regards the offence, it is quite the opposite.'

He paused again, whether he felt the necessity to reflect, or whether he simply desired to hurry on with telling his beads.

'When did the white man go and get his jacket back?' he asked the beggar.

'I don't know,' said the beggar. 'The white man never left me.'

'He never left you?' asked the judge.

'He never left me for a moment,' said the beggar.

'Good! I conclude from that that you were with him when he returned to the lodging-house. Must I understand that you were his accomplice?'

'I am not his accomplice,' said the beggar.

'Exactly!' said the judge. 'You are simply the witness for the prosecution. What have you to say on the indictment of the white man?'

'I was never more than a foot away from him,' said the beggar.

'Again?' said the judge. 'Be careful: you are going to get yourself into trouble!'

'Then, I have nothing at all to say,' said the beggar.

'What!' exclaimed Clarence. 'Won't you maintain that we never left each other?'

'Silence!' cried the judge. 'Do not try to influence the witness. He has chosen to say nothing; if it is not very brave of him, it is at least within his rights. Certainly his silence overwhelms you; but think, his words might be even more disastrous for you. Be satisfied then with the lesser evil. . . . Now, let's see! What reasons can you give for having taken the jacket back?'

'He gave it to me against his will,' said the landlord.

'That is in fact what the white man declared in my presence,' said the chief guard.

'Is that so?' the judge asked Clarence.

'Why should it not be so?' cried Clarence. 'It is quite true that I gave him my jacket unwillingly.'

'But he took it back willingly enough,' said the landlord.

'It's not your turn to speak!' said the judge. 'If you interrupt me again I'll have you turned out of court. And don't you go making jokes here; that's the privilege of the bench and of the bench alone. And don't let me have to tell you again.'

'May I ask you, Your Honour, the Chief Magistrate,' asked Clarence, 'whether you would have given up your jacket willingly?'

'It is not your business to ask me questions,' said the judge. 'An accused, even when he might be presumed innocent—but that would be so paradoxical that I refuse to entertain the possibility—an accused must never ask questions: it is quite contrary to custom. Besides, you must admit it would be far too convenient. At the most I might tolerate an interrogative turn of phrase, if this was duly accompanied by the reply, but this is not the case here. However, to do you a favour, and for this once only, I consent to depart from the custom, and consequently to answer your question. The answer is: "No, I for my part would never have parted with my jacket either willingly or unwillingly, for the excellent reason that I never wear one!" Are you satisfied? . . . And now that I can see you are definitely determined not to give back the jacket, will you be good enough to tell me how you intend to indemnify the landlord?'

'But . . . ' said Clarence.

'Do not force me to put you in prison,' said the judge. 'I have never yet put a white man behind bars. I can assure you that I should find it most painful.'

'I will indemnify this man as soon as I have a job. That was in fact my original intention.'

'That was, and is still, a very praiseworthy intention,' said the judge. 'But are you really out of a job? And if so, when will you find one?'

'I was just off to the South to find a job.'

'Indeed?' said the judge.

'I intend to ask the king for a job.'

'The king?' said the judge.

He seemed surprised. He was so surprised that he forgot to tell his beads.

'Listen, my good friend,' he continued after a moment. 'That smacks of complete crookery to me. What sort of a job could the king entrust to you? And even if he found one for you—which I doubt very much—when would you repay the landlord? The king has only just returned to his palace, so he is not likely to be setting out for the South again just yet. . . . But enough said. Up to now your offence has been a minor fraud, so do not think to improve your position by turning it into a full-scale swindle. Consequently, come back to my question, which was intended to get you out of your difficulties; what do you suggest by way of compensation to the landlord?'

'If the white man agrees to give me his shirt and trousers, I'll let him off with the jacket,' said the landlord.

'That is a very fair proposal,' said the judge.

'Fair?' remarked Clarence.

'Certainly, very fair,' said the judge. 'While he was about it he might have demanded your socks and shoes as well; but he stopped at your shirt and trousers.'

'Can you see me walking about naked in the streets?' asked Clarence.

'There is no law against it,' said the judge, 'and there is no lack of people with no sense of shame. If, as you state, you are making for the South, you'll meet plenty of such impudent folk. . . . And let me tell you that you did not show a very considerable sense of shame when you took the jacket back from the landlord. . . . Anyway, there is no question of your going about naked. White men usually wear underpants under their shirt.'

'Very brief underpants, and . . . . '

'Then be sure that they are properly fastened,' said the judge.

'These intimate details are no concern of a Chief Magistrate . . . Guards !'

'At your orders, Your Honour, the Chief Magistrate,' answered the guard with the rope.

'Order the court to rise to hear the sentence.'

The guard with the cord turned with his acolytes towards the empty room. While he was lining up his men—and under the circumstances, the ranks had to be in perfect order—the beggar surreptitiously approached Clarence and whispered in his ear :

'Run ! Don't wait ! Run ! Meet me at the gate of the city.'

'But . . . .'

'Run, I tell you, or they'll have your underpants as well ! . . . Can't you see the Chief Magistrate is in league with the landlord? . . . You're forgetting that there will be the legal costs !'

It was the thought of the legal costs, and naturally, of his underpants in which they would be materialized, which decided Clarence. The trousers, the shirt even, Clarence was resigned to their loss. But his underpants? Could he reasonably be separated from his underpants? . . . He bolted like a hare, and found himself in the corridor before the others had realized what was happening. When they had recovered their presence of mind—and the landlord seemed to be the first to recover, unless it was the judge . . . but his Chief Magistrate's dignity prevented him leaving his table— when they had recovered their presence of mind, they all collided so madly in the doorway that each one seemed temporarily to abandon all hope of catching the fugitive. They would obviously catch him sooner or later : the crowd outside was so thick that their search would be immediately rewarded.

'Take your men and search the town,' said the judge to the chief guard. 'I am not leaving my table till you bring me back the fugitive. And this time, tie him up.'

Clarence, in the meantime, had opened at random one of the hundred doors which gave on to the corridor. And now he was fleeing through a maze of deserted rooms and empty passages. And as he ran, spurred on as he was by the fear of losing his underpants, he never ceased to marvel at the accumulation of rooms and passages in a building, which seen from the outside, or at least, glimpsed in the doubtful gleam of the night, had seemed hardly much bigger than the other houses of the town. For a moment he even suspected that he was continually crossing the same rooms and the same passages but he did not stop long at this hypothesis. For the moment he had something else to do !

Among other things, he was busy avoiding an incredible quantity of rubbish and builders' rubble, which appeared to be either torn down from the thatch by the storm or crumbled directly away from the decaying walls. And there was not only the rubbish and rubble in all these interleading rooms and endless passages : there were actually heaps of earth, improbable heaps of earth, as if the owner of the property, despairing of the state of his roof and walls, had suddenly given up all idea of repairing them and had started to rebuild. Apparently that was it. Otherwise how could you account for so much refuse of all kinds accumulated in these rooms and passages? So much refuse, indeed, that you could well believe that all the housewives of the neighbourhood had sent round the word to empty their dustbins here ; which was most uncomplimentary to the justice, or injustice—Clarence voted for injustice—that the judges were presumed to render in these precincts.

But where, in fact, was Clarence? Where had Clarence got to after traversing so many rooms and passages and surmounting so many obstacles just in time? Was he still in the court building? Or was he not already at the other end of the town? One door that he opened, after having opened so many others, made him nearly cry out in despair ; the door opened on to that same court room from which he had fled so many hours or so many seconds earlier.

He stopped short, gasping for breath and bent double as if one of the guards had given him a kick or a punch full in the stomach. Then he saw that the room was deserted except for the judge squatting on his table ; squatting in the same position exactly in which Clarence had left him, but not in the same frame of mind, for now the old rascal appeared harmless enough. He was asleep, and snoring, and with what sonorous majesty ! 'What a sleep !' thought Clarence. 'The sleep of the just !' Softly he tiptoed away ; he went out into the corridor which he followed to the end without a glance at the innumerable doors. . . . And with a sigh of relief he found himself once more in the street, in the red glow of the fires, in the uproar of the street.

Translator's note: Clarence makes his way slowly through the throngs till one of the dancing women recognizes him and leads him to a house where he finds the beggar awaiting him with the two young lads. The latter are seen to be wearing, under their tunics, half each of the missing jacket, which they, in fact, had stolen back from the innkeeper in order to share between them.

A Night on the Island

S. F. ABODERIN

🌺

IT was the fishing season. Along the southern coast of the Olorunda Island there were people laughing and talking on the sandy beaches. The women were telling each other stories of mermaids and other animals which had lived in the sea. Now you can hear the fishermen's songs, coming out from different boats on the sea.

The sun had quickly set. The waves began to quicken, and then the hollow, sadly majestic tide of evening swallowed up the girls' voices and their giggling laughter, and now they began to think of returning home. Meanwhile they stared vaguely across the sea towards the fishermen. In their hearts they mildly accused them of being late, but the boats were returning while the worn-out evening glowed on their sails.

Before long the whole coast was lined up with fishing boats. With a sudden roar all the women and children swarmed towards the boats. They were like maddened bees in their desire to reach the fish. They joked as they lifted the fish in their hands. There were some with sharp tails, and others were with mouths wide open and gazing in wonder.

At that moment Abudu, who was naked to the waist, forced his way through the crowd and leapt on to Lawani's boat. Without a word he proceeded to gather up the fish.

Lawani went up to him and held him by the arm. 'Pay your money first,' he said. 'Then you can gather the fish.'

'I'll pay you next time,' Abudu said without giving him a glance.

'That won't do.'

'No?' he retorted. Abudu had stood up straight and glared at Lawani angrily.

'When I say it won't do, it won't do. It's broad daylight now,' Lawani said, staring back at him. 'Are you going to steal?'

'All right—just step off the boat,' Abudu shouted, jumping ashore and throwing down a challenge for fight.

'All right, I have no objection. See what you can do,' Lawani answered, and followed him ashore. Abudu quickly struck his opponent a blow which sent him reeling. Lawani tried to keep his balance, but he fell down.

The crowd heard them and gathered round. The islanders enjoyed a fight as much as town people do. No one separated them. Lawani got to his feet, feeling ashamed of himself, but suddenly he darted forward and struck out at Abudu's head. It was a heavy blow, but Abudu raised his arm and warded it off. Then Lawani kicked Abudu in the ribs with his left foot, and Abudu, forced to retreat a little, managed to catch hold of the foot. It was all over then. Lawani was on the ground again, face upward, like a frog. He quickly got up but was dropped to the ground again, his nose rubbing against the ground. He had been publicly disgraced and had to go home.

When darkness crept over the island from the sea, no one was left on the beach. From afar, in the village, came the sound of fish-sellers, and their lanterns glittered in the dark alleys. By the time the night watchman had struck the second watch, Abudu's load of fish had changed into money which reposed in his waist bag. Smelling of fish all over, he went to knock at Modupe's gate. The heavy taps on the wooden door woke up the dogs in the neighbourhood. Their barking became contagious and soon the whole island reverberated with the sounds of barking.

'Who is that, coming to disturb his old mother's sleep?'

'Your old boy. Open it quick.'

'Oh! I wondered who it was. The old boy, eh? You come in the nick of time. Your old mother was asleep and longing for you,' Modupe answered, opening the gate.

Abudu entered, inspected the room, grumbling. The bedding was rough, the pillow fattened. He dropped down on the bed, face upward, and gnashed his teeth. Modupe, with her hair unloosened, sat by his side. She threw herself against him. 'Good heavens, where did you steal this money which gives your mother such a bump on the body? Let me count it for you,' she said, untying the bag from Abudu's waist belt. Standing by the light she counted the money in fives and tens. 'There are three hundred and fifty coppers and two counterfeits,' she said as she had finished counting.

Abudu replied: 'There are over five hundred there. Whenever money passes through your hands it gets less.' They both smiled simultaneously and the lights in the room were put out.

This is an island which has been regarded as uncivilized. The threat to kill is characteristic of its inhabitants. The resolution passed through their minds quickly, and, at times, it needed no prompting. Lawani had planned a revenge—a brutal one indeed. The crescent moon was shining on the island. Lawani had invited ten of his neighbours for the revenge. They feasted on the pig's head and drank wine. Suddenly, there arose a sound of disordered footsteps. Eleven strong men with fishing-forks, knives, sticks and clubs in their hands proceeded to Modupe's house. There was a wave of shouts and knockings which awoke the neighbours. The noise grew louder and more insistent. After a long while Modupe questioned them.

'Open the gate quickly. We are looking for Abudu,' they shouted.

'Oh! so you are looking for him? He stopped coming here a long time ago. I haven't seen his shadow lately.' While she was speaking a tall man jumped over the back wall and disappeared.

'Open it quickly—quickly.'

'Stop your mouth.'

'Quickly, quickly, or we'll kick your gate down.' The voices from outside grew more urgent.

'I won't open it, I won't open it. If you break down the door, you'll have to pay for it.'

'Let's jump over the wall,' someone shouted.

With a violent creak she opened the door. 'Come in, if you want to come in, come in, I dare say. What's all the fuss about?'

They crowded inside. There was tumult. They searched the bedding, behind the door, under the table, inside the chest. There was nothing.

As they rushed out to look for him elsewhere one of them that had lingered after them shouted, 'Come back, come back.' He had picked up a red cap at the foot of the bed and on close examination they recognized it was Abudu's cap. A sense of righteousness and revenge came over them. What followed was a shout of 'Tie her up. Demand the man from her.' 'Beat her, torture her, demand the man from her.'

They seized her and she told them: 'Don't display your bravery before me, I hid him. What about it? Let me tell you the truth. I sent him away while you were making all the row here.'

They looked at one another. Their faces expressed a mixture of emotions: surprise, anger, contempt, the sense of having been mocked at, revenge. All these emotions found their target on the woman, and the venom they had intended for Abudu was thrown at her. The wine in their stomachs had to find some outlet. So they decided to do to Modupe what they had previously decided to do to Abudu.

As she was dragged towards the sea, she cursed and called them names. While she was cursing, they drew near to the shore and now she stopped cursing and only sobbed. At the shore, they tied her four limbs behind her back, like tying the four ends of a handker-chief into a knot. They brought out the sackcloth bag they had prepared beforehand, and they were about to put her in, when there suddenly appeared from behind them a tall man, and he shouted : 'Stop, what crime has she committed?'

They turned in amazement, and in the light of the slanting moon they recognized Abudu. Their surprise was complete, but when they noticed that he had no weapons with him their courage returned, and they began to turn towards him, armed with their fishing-forks, knives, sticks and clubs, ready to attack.

Abudu said coldly : 'No fighting is needed. Set her free and bind me up. I stole the fish, not she.' As soon as he said this, he turned his back to them, crossed his arms behind his back and allowed them to bind him up. At first they were dumbfounded, but imme-diately afterwards they closed on him and tied up his arms. Abudu made no movement and said nothing.

They put him into the sackcloth bag and then fastened a rock to it. Four of them carried it to a waiting boat. They steered out to sea, yelling a battle-cry, and then they threw the bag overboard. The sackcloth bag described large circular waves, which expanded and multiplied until at last the thin circles disappeared.

The men went away. The moon was going down now and shining on Modupe, who sat on the shore like a rock, gazing steadily out to the sea.

Truth and Falsehood

BIRAGO DIOP

Translated from the French by Dorothy Blair

FENE-FALSEHOOD had grown big and had learnt many things. But there were many things that he still did not know, notably that man—and woman even less—bears no resemblance to the good Lord. And so he took umbrage and considered himself hard done by every time he heard any one say : 'The good Lord loves Truth !' and he heard it very often. Some certainly said that nothing looks more like the truth than a falsehood, but the majority stated that Truth and Falsehood were like night and day. That is why, when one day he set out on a journey with Deug-Truth, Fene-Falsehood said to his travelling companion :

'You are the one whom the Lord loves, you are the one whom people no doubt prefer, so it is you who must do the talking everywhere we go. For if I were recognized we should be very badly received.'

They set out early in the morning and walked for a long time. At midday they entered the first house of the village which they reached. After they had exchanged greetings they had to ask before being given anything to drink. The mistress of the house gave them, in a calabash of doubtful cleanliness, some lukewarm water which would have made an ostrich vomit. There was no question of giving them anything to eat, although a pot full of rice was boiling at the entrance to the hut. The travellers lay down in the shade of a baobab in the middle of the courtyard and awaited the good Lord, that is to say, luck and the return of the master of the house. The latter came back at twilight and asked for food for himself and the strangers.

'I haven't got anything ready yet,' said the woman, who could not have swallowed by herself the whole contents of the pot.

The husband flew into a great rage, not only on his own account, although he was famished after having spent the whole day working in the fields in the blazing sun, but because of his unknown guests, whom he was unable to honour (as every master of the house worthy of the name should do) and who had been left with empty bellies. He asked :

'Is that the action of a good wife? Is that the action of a generous woman? Is that a good housewife?'

Fene-Falsehood, as agreed, prudently said nothing, but Deug-Truth could not keep silent. She answered sincerely that a woman worthy of the name of mistress of the house might have been more hospitable to strangers, and ought always to have something prepared for her husband's return.

Then the woman flew into a mad rage and, threatening to arouse the whole village, ordered her husband to throw out these impertinent strangers, who interfered in the way she ran her house and took it upon themselves to give her advice, otherwise she would return home to her parents on the spot. So the poor husband, who could not see himself managing without a wife (even a bad housekeeper) and without any cooking because of two strangers, two passers-by whom he had never seen and whom he would probably never see again in his life, was forced to tell the travellers to be on their way. Did they not remember, these ill-bred travellers, that life was not all *couscous*,[1] but that it did need some softening, however? Did they have to say things so crudely?

So Deug and Fene continued their journey which had begun so ill. They walked on for a long time and reached a village in the entrance to which they found some children busy sharing out a fat bull which they had just slaughtered. On entering the house of the village chief, they saw some children who were saying to him:

'Here is your share,' and they gave him the head and the feet of the animal.

Now, since time immemorial, since n'Diadiane n'Diaye, in every village inhabited by man, it is the chief who gives every one his share, and who chooses his own—the best.

'Who do you think commands here in this village?' the chief asked the travellers.

Prudently Fene-Falsehood kept silent and did not open his mouth: Deug-Truth was obliged, as agreed, to give her opinion:

'To all appearances,' she said, 'it is these children.'

'You are insolent folk!' cried the old man in a rage. 'Leave this village, go, go immediately, or else you will never leave it again! Begone, begone!'

And the unfortunate travellers continued on their way.

As they went, Fene said to Deug:

'The results have not been very brilliant so far, and I am not sure if they will be any better if I go on any longer leaving you in charge of our affairs. So from now on I am going to look after both of us. I am beginning to think that even if the good Lord loves you, man doesn't appreciate you over much.'

Not knowing how they would be received in the village they were approaching, and from whence came cries and lamentations, Deug and Fene stopped at the well before entering any dwelling, and were quenching their thirst, when a woman came along all in tears.

'What is the meaning of these cries and tears?' asked Deug-Truth.

'Alas!' said the woman (she was a slave) 'our favourite queen, the youngest of the king's wives, died yesterday, and the king is so heart-sore that he wishes to kill himself, so that he may rejoin the woman who was the fairest and most gracious of his wives.'

'And is that the sole cause of so much lamenting?' asked Fene-Falsehood. 'Go tell the king that there is at the well a stranger who can bring back to life people who have even been dead for long.'

The slave went off and returned a minute later accompanied by

[1] Food made from millet or guinea corn.

an old man who led the travellers into a fine hut, where they found a whole sheep roasted and two calabashes of *couscous*.

'My master brings you here,' said the old man, 'and bids you rest after your long journey. He bids you wait and he will send for you ere long.'

The next day an even more copious repast was brought to the strangers, and the day after the same thing happened. But Fene pretended to be angry and impatient; he said to the messenger:

'Go tell your king that I have no time to waste here, and that I shall continue on my way if he has no need of me.'

The old man returned, telling him:

'The king is asking for you.' And Fene followed him, leaving Deug-Truth in the hut.

'First, what do you desire as a reward for what you are about to do?' asked the king, when he came before him.

'What can you offer me?' replied Fene-Falsehood.

'I will give you one hundred things from all that I possess in this land.'

'That will not satisfy me,' calculated Fene.

'Say then yourself what you desire,' suggested the king.

'I desire the half of all that you possess.'

'That is agreed,' the king accepted.

Fene had a hut built above the grave of the favourite, and went in alone, armed with a hoe. He could be heard puffing and panting; then, after a very long time, he began to talk, softly at first, then in a very loud voice as if he were arguing with several persons; at length he came out of the hut and stood with his back firmly pressed against the door.

'Things are getting very complicated,' he said to the king. 'I have dug up the grave, I have woken your wife, but scarcely had she returned to life and was about to emerge from beneath the ground than your father woke up too and seized her by the feet, saying to me: "Leave this woman alone. What can she give to you? Whereas if I return to earth, I will give you all the fortune of my son." He had barely finished making me this proposition than his father emerged in his turn and offered me all his goods and half the property of his son. Your grandfather was elbowed out of the way by the grandfather of your father, who offered me your property, your father's property, his son's property and the half of his own fortune. Scarcely had he finished speaking than his father arrived, so that your ancestors and the forbears of their ancestors are all at the exit of your wife's grave.'

The King Bour looked at his advisers, and the notables looked at the king. The stranger was quite right to say that things were in a mess. Bour gazed at Fene-Falsehood, and the old men gazed at him. What was to be done?

'To help you out of your dilemma, and to avoid too difficult a choice,' said Fene-Falsehood, 'just give me an idea which I should bring back, your wife or your father?'

'My wife!' said the king, who loved the favourite more than ever and who had always been afraid of the late king, whose death he had precipitated, with the assistance of the notables.

'Naturally, naturally!' replied Fene-Falsehood. 'Only, you see, your father did offer me double what you promised me just now.'

Bour turned towards his advisers, and the advisers gazed at him and gazed at the stranger. The price was high, and what good would it do the king to see his most beloved wife again, if he were deprived of all his goods? Would he still be king? Fene guessed the thoughts of the king and of his notables :

'Unless,' he said, 'unless you give me, for leaving your wife where she is at present, what you promised me to bring her back.'

'That is certainly the best and the most reasonable thing to do!' replied in chorus the old notables who had contributed to the disappearance of the old king.

'What do you say, Bour?' asked Fene-Falsehood.

'Oh, well, let my father, the father of my father and the fathers of their fathers remain where they are, and my wife likewise,' said the king.

And so it was that Fene-Falsehood, for bringing no one back from the other world, received half the property of the king, who, moreover, soon forgot his favourite and took another wife.

The Talking Skull

A NUPE FOLK TALE

A HUNTER goes into the bush. He finds an old human skull. The hunter says : 'What brought you here?' The skull answers : 'Talking brought me here.' The hunter runs off. He runs to the king. He tells the king : 'I found a dry human skull in the bush. It asks you how its father and mother are.'

The king says : 'Never since my mother bore me have I heard that a dead skull can speak.' The king summons the Alkali, the Saba, and the Degi and asks them if they have ever heard the like. None of the wise men has heard the like and they decide to send a guard out with the hunter into the bush to find out if his story is true and, if so, to learn the reason for it. The guard accompany the hunter into the bush with the order to kill him on the spot should he have lied. The guard and the hunter come to the skull. The hunter addresses the skull : 'Skull, speak.' The skull is silent. The hunter asks as before : 'What brought you here?' The skull does not answer. The whole day long the hunter begs the skull to speak, but it does not answer. In the evening the guard tell the hunter to make the skull speak, and when he cannot they kill him in accordance with the king's command. When the guard are gone the skull opens its jaws and asks the dead hunter's head : 'What brought you here?' The dead hunter's head replies : 'Talking brought me here !'

Ritual Murder

C. O. D. EKWENSI

THE two black men were afraid. Kofi could read it in their eyes. They did not wish to leave him. They stood on the steps of the palace, stubbornly loyal.

'We will wait for you here,' they said. 'We are your bodyguard. Your wife said we must not lose sight of you.'

'There's no need, brothers. I'm quite safe.'

They came nearer, their arms gesturing wildly. 'You make light of the danger, Kofi.'

'Nothing can happen to me.' Kofi slung the velvet robe over one shoulder. 'Do not fear. A new paramount chief is in office, true . . . .'

'And he will wash the golden stool with human blood. Maybe yours . . . .'

Kofi laughed.

They were uneasy. 'But, Kofi . . . Look! . . . Can't you understand?'

It was useless. Kofi had mounted the steps, and the door of the palace had opened and shut.

'He's mad,' said one, shrugging. The other one scowled at him for a while. 'Yes . . . really mad.'

In the distance the West African sunshine blazed downwards. Two girls hawking biscuits strolled past the palace, their cotton dresses a feast of colour. They made eyes at the two men on the steps. Cars, lorries, hand-trucks, horse-drawn carts, were moving along the street. A policeman was directing the traffic, and he paused to show a white man the right road. It was impossible to contemplate ancient evil beneath this façade of Western law and order. Surely no harm could come to Kofi.

Kofi followed the guide through a dark corridor.

'They're expecting you,' the guide said. 'You'll find them in the black room.'

'The black room?'

'Yes . . . .'

The room where, away from the eyes of the law, gruesome rites were performed; wherein stood the golden stool waiting, always waiting for a new *Omanhene* [1] to die, so that a new one might wash it with blood. In the dark days, a slave's blood was easy to come by. But not now. The white men frowned on the use of human blood. For years the blood of a dove, a sheep, had provided a legal substitute.

The guide said: 'Knock on the door. I leave you.'

Kofi looked at the massive door. He looked behind him at the dark corridor. He was alone. There was no turning back. He flung his shoulders back and breathed deeply. His knees were trembling. He knocked. No one answered; but the door gave when he pushed and he went in.

At a table in the centre of the room, six men were playing cards. The air smelled strongly of spirits. They turned and looked at Kofi grimly, their hard bare torsos etched out by the smoky hurricane lamp.

'Shut the door and sit down, Kofi.' They indicated an empty seat at the table. A whole bottle of raw gin was pushed across to him. 'Drink some! . . . it isn't poisoned!'

He was uncomfortable. He held his breath in the stuffy atmosphere. The mystery, the suspense, the secrecy irritated him. He did not wish to be a party to anything furtive.

'I am here now,' he said. 'What did you want me for?'

Apiedu, the eldest of the half-brothers, waved aside Kofi's fears. 'Have patience, my boy,' he soothed. 'You'll soon know.'

'I haven't got all day . . . there's work to do. The old *Omanhene,* your father, is dead. His affairs are in disorder. It is my duty . . .'

'We know you were his secretary. And that is why we sent for you. With your intimate knowledge of his private affairs, you are going to be very useful. You will be well paid, of course, if you co-operate.'

They passed the raw gin round, and each of them sucked from the bottle and handed it to the next man. Kofi glanced about him uneasily. In a corner of the room, he could barely see the golden stool. It was not so golden now, with the dark stains on it. On top of the stool was a wickedly sharp knife . . . the *saw-paw* of the ritual murders. It was the same knife that had buried itself in the hearts of many a slave some half a century ago.

'Kofi,' said Apiedu. 'We want to ask you a little favour.'

'Go ahead.'

'It's about that money,' Apiedu said. 'Come, Kofi! You know about it!'

[1] A chief or head of a state in Ashanti.

Kofi swallowed. 'I . . . I . . . .'

'Ten thousand pounds. . . . My father took it out of the treasury and founded "Kofo and Co." Everybody in the smallest village in West Africa knows about it. Of course the business is doing very well. But the new *Omanhene* may not like it; just as he may not like to take over our father's wives. He'll make changes. He'll tell the Government what happened. Where will we be then?'

Kofi said nothing. Apiedu glanced round the table. His brothers were dealing out cards with half an ear on the discussion.

'Ten thousand pounds is a lot of money for the auditors to overlook. And now, Kofi, what are *you* going to do about it?'

'Me? I . . . I don't understand . . . '

'It's easy! You are the only man in Africa who has access to the fatal papers. You alone can dig up the evidence the new *Omanhene* might want if he decides to make trouble. Got that? Well, we're asking a very simple favour. We want you to go back and destroy every scrap of evidence pointing to the theft of that ten thousand.'

'I . . . I can't. It isn't my business to audit accounts. I have nothing to do with the money of the state.'

'That's right! . . . You have nothing to do with it, but you know where to find the rope that will hang us. Go and burn that rope.' The brothers had stopped playing their game. 'If you talk too much, Kofo and Co. will be given to the state. We will go to jail. There'll be hard work to do . . . .' He glanced at his soft hands. 'We have never worked in our lives, and it is too late to start now. Why do you look so worried? This is but a little favour we have asked of you. And your reward is . . . two thousand pounds!'

Kofi looked at them helplessly. It was true he knew about that deal: every single man involved in it. And he knew many more things besides. He could make life completely intolerable for the late chief's sons. He looked up. The light threw dark shadows on their faces. Their eyes were hard, unforgiving. He saw them through the smoky haze of the lamp, and somehow tried to fight against the mad idea that this was unreal, a mere dream.

'Give me time,' he begged. 'I have not yet come to that business. When I come to it, I'll know how to fix things.'

The brothers exchanged glances. No one spoke.

'I . . . I don't think there is anything more,' Kofi said, rising. 'I must go now. Don't worry! Everything will be all right.'

Did they believe him? The room was so still that he wanted to shout at them. Slowly he backed towards the door.

'Where are you going, Kofi?'

They were all standing now.

'Don't you trust me? I've told you . . . there's nothing to worry about. Let me go home to my wife and children.'

Apiedu laughed. 'He's going home. Ha! ha! . . . And we'll be here . . . waiting!'

Panic seized Kofi. He had sensed something sinister beneath it all. In a sudden burst of recklessness he sprang for the door. But he was too late. They were between him and the massive structure. And he knew then that they meant to murder him.

'What did you want to do?' Apiedu said softly. 'To go out and betray us?'

'Go and sit down,' said Lampey.

Kofi stood his ground. 'You cannot frighten me,' he bluffed. 'I came to the palace gate with two men. Your own guide brought me to this door. My wife knows where I am. If you do anything to me, everybody will know. Go back to your drink and don't touch me. You'll only regret it. I've given you my word : everything will be all right.'

'Nonsense!' said Apiedu.

Kofi did a very foolish thing. Perhaps he thought he was being brave. He pushed Lampey aside and seized the door handle. Almost at once, something hard struck him on the back of the head, and he fell against the door and slid downwards.

'Bring him over to this corner,' said Apiedu.

'But he's not dead.'

'That's just it . . . his blood will be still warm . . . for the stool.'

'We'll all hang!' said Kwame, the youngest brother. 'God knows I am innocent.'

'You can't prove it,' Apiedu said. 'We've done this thing to help you. Nobody will ever suspect us. Why would we want to kill any one? We have no motive. But the new *Omanhene,* he has . . . he wants to wash the stool . . . an age-old ritual. And he kills Kofi. He cannot tell the white men, because no one will believe him. His hands are tied. And remember this : he has been boasting that he will not use pigeon's blood, or sheep's blood . . . so we're all right!'

'He's dead,' said Lampey, who had been holding him.

Silence fell in the room.

'Two of you go for a cart,' Apiedu said. 'Hide it somewhere. As soon as it is dark we'll take the body away.'

Kwame paced up and down the little room.

'You're frightened, Kwame.'

'I've never seen a man killed before!'

Apiedu smiled. 'Yes! But there's a reason, Kwame! Either we put this new *Omanhene* into trouble, or he puts us. There's no other way. We must live!'

'I don't want to live in that way. Let me work till my hands peel rather than kill a man and . . . and use his blood.'

'Shut up, Kwame!'

Kwame pulled up, sweating and trembling. The others did not move.

Under the palm trees, in the market places, men and women talked about the missing official. With lips scarcely open, they hissed out the terrible word : *murder*.

'The *Omanhene* has killed Kofi, now he wants us to help him look for the man he has killed and buried.'

And away on the rolling grassland where the nomads grazed their cattle, Apiedu was amusing his brothers.

'The police are so stupid! Look what a fuss they made about those drops of blood in the black room : giving it to the Government pathologist to analyse and to prove it was human blood. What else could it be?' He laughed. 'But there's no blood without a body! Where is Kofi?'

'They will catch us,' Kwame said. 'We are wasting time by hiding here.'

Fear and hunger had worn him down.

'We are safe here,' Apiedu said.

'Yes,' put in the others.

Kwame spat. 'They will catch us. If not to-day, to-morrow. But they will surely hang all of us . . . .' He broke off suddenly.

'Look! . .' he panted. 'See him!'

The brothers looked, but there was nothing to see. Kwame was gazing at the door of the hut, his face working.

'He is going mad,' Apiedu said uneasily. 'Sometimes he hears the voice of our father . . . sometimes he sees the spirit of Kofi.'

'Who knows?' said Lampey. 'Perhaps he may be seeing something.'

Apiedu looked startled. 'You too? Are you getting the fever?'

That night, after they had retired to their grass beds, Lampey suddenly cried out. 'He's lying on my bed. . . . He's here! . . .'

A light was fetched. 'Where is he?' said Apiedu.

'He was here in the bed beside me. I swear! I wouldn't deceive you, would I, Apiedu?'

Apiedu looked at him scornfully. 'You are even worse than the boy, Lampey! Who's next?'

'He . . . he was here,' said Lampey. 'He lay beside me on this bed!'

'Yes,' Apiedu said, 'but where is he now?'

Lampey looked foolish. He had scared the whole party and now they crowded together around the lantern, and kept vigil the whole night through.

Long before dawn, Apiedu went out into the grassland. It was chilly. A mist hung in the air. In this lonely part of the veld no one was about. Their only contact was the next village where Lampey sometimes went to buy food. It seemed that the hard life, the fear of the police, the contemplation of the future which held nothing for them, was troubling his brothers. Something had to be done, and soon too.

He paused and looked about him. Somewhere ahead of him, leaning against a tree, was a dark figure. It was a man. Who could it be, at this early hour and in so lonely a place? Apiedu walked on, and the figure detached itself from the tree and moved quickly towards him, forcing him to step out of the narrow footpath.

The black man in the dark cloth passed him like a flash and disappeared behind the bend. The mist hung thick. The air seemed to become more chilly. It could have been a dream, if he had not noted that bare bald head, those bulging eyes.

Back in the little hut, he asked Lampey whether they had a visitor.

'No,' said Lampey.

Apiedu described the encounter as lightly as he could and dismissed it. But Lampey returned to the subject.

'Apiedu, you may be a very brave man; but let us go to Koforidua . . . to the fetishman. We can consult him about this evil spirit.'

'Yes,' said Kwame. 'I was about to say the same, but I was afraid you would laugh at me.'

'It is the best thing,' agreed the others.

The three brothers entered the hut of the fetishman stealthily.

'You wish to make a confession?' said the priest. 'Sit down!'

'We are haunted,' Apiedu said.

'We cannot sleep,' Lampey added. 'At night, the man we killed comes. Sometimes he sleeps beside one of us.' He shivered.

'And you want something to drive off this evil spirit?'

'Yes.'

'I shall give you a powder to burn. But the preparation of this powder requires one very special ingredient. It may be too late to get it. Then I can do nothing. Something from the dead man's body.'

Apiedu looked uneasily round. 'We buried him . . . .'

'Yes, I know. Long ago?'

'Three weeks. What do you want? Tell me, I'll get it for you . . . '

The old man smiled. 'That would destroy everything. I have to get it myself. You will come with me, and you will bring with you digging implements. It will have to be at night. No one will see us.'

Apiedu said: 'I . . . I must consult my brothers first. I . . . .'

'If you are afraid, let things lie. In my business privacy comes first. You can be sure I shall not discuss your affairs with anyone.'

When they had gone, the fetishman looked up his manuscripts. It was a long time since he had handled a case of haunting.

The door darkened. New clients? But these two, the white man in plain clothes and the black man in a black robe, were not clients.

'I am a police officer,' said the white man. 'May I come in?'

'This is the new *Omanhene*. We have reason to believe that the sons of the late *Omanhene* visited you not long ago.'

'Yes,' said the *Omanhene*. 'What did they tell you?'

'Long may you reign, chief! They were having stomach trouble.' The fetishman smiled.

The white man smiled. 'Those six boys are murderers. They have framed your chief here. We have no evidence against them. If you do not say what you know I will take it that you are a party to the crime. And in that case, I must ask you to come with me to the station. The car is outside.'

'What do you want to know?'

'Just what you know.'

'It is against my practice . . . but those boys are haunted.'

The white man tapped the *Omanhene* on the shoulder. 'And this is the ghost who did all the haunting. For three weeks he has been watching the brothers.'

The fetishman's mouth widened. Then he grinned. 'I see. So he is the ghost? Now, these boys want my help, and I want something —from the body. If they agree, they will take me to the spot to-night. If not . . .'

'I'm sure they'll come,' the white man said. 'And we'll be there, too! They won't know, of course.'

'I knew they couldn't stand it,' the *Omanhene* said. 'Kwame was the first to break; the last was Apiedu.'

'The reward for their capture is three hundred pounds,' the police officer said.

'I do not want your money.'

In the night the brothers slipped into the hut. They were wearing long dark caps pulled low over their eyes. 'It is chilly outside,' said Apiedu. 'We are here, now. Let us go quickly!'

The fetishman put on a cape woven from elephant grass. 'You'll have to carry me,' he said. 'I'm lame.'

131

The brothers took him into the valley where a stream trickled over the sands. Kwame was shivering.

'The body is there,' Apiedu said, 'under the stream. We stemmed the water, then dug a hole and buried him. After that, we let the water flow over him.'

'You can do the same now,' said the old man. 'You've got your tools?'

'Yes, we have our tools.'

'You will have to excuse me while you work.'

The fetishman turned away. He limped up the valley. The white man was in police uniform now. And so was every man in the party behind him. He did not speak to them.

From a bag under his arm he drew out a little packet and poured a powder down his throat.

'Eighty years,' he muttered, 'and I have never betrayed anyone.' He sank on his knees, waiting for the poison to act.

Marriage Cordiality

C. ENITAN BROWN

The day was a Thursday, grand was the marriage,
When blooming flowers of Lagos trooped out on parade;
Drums and cymbals, cornets blazing rapturous music with a
  din;
The sun tarried long and beheld the scene:
Colours gay and cool-pink and blue, green and grey
Forming shoes and neck-scarves
Frocks in white array—
The latest word in fashion of feminine dresses
Depicting well the skill and toil of
Lagos sempstresses.

A sea of round heads crowned with black and glistering hair
Rolled up over the neck, caressing the ear
Numerous high heels trump'd along many in each row,
Bare legs below skirts that flit to and fro
Dancing in harmony with hips round or broad.
Backs straight as a bat, necks round like a rod,
Waistline an ellipse, white teeth of steaming ladies
Whose smiles reveal the carefree thought behind those charm-
  ing faces.

Flowers of the field are pleasant to watch,
Oh! it is just enough to compare the sight
Along that Broad Street to flowers on the march
As blooming flowers attract butterflies in flight
To partake of their beauty and their fragrance rich and sweet,
No less did dancing belles attract to their company
Budding Lagos manhood, along our Broad Street,
On that day of marriage cordiality.

Shadow of Darkness

GLADYS CASELY-HAYFORD

'HE is called Shadow of Darkness, for he is as powerful as the darkness: his temple is evil as a spirit of darkness: his pelt is the colour of darkness. He has on his forehead a white triangular spot, on his back an eagle, and a beetle hump is under his tongue.'

Thus spoke Jalona, the Fullah lad, the youngest herdsman of the group, his thin, handsome face quivering in the light of the camp fire. His pale copper colour was a strange contrast to the almost black skin of his confederates. His chest, which gave promise of great breadth in manhood, rose and fell with pride. His lids drew down over his proud eyes, revealing the long lashes which swept his cheeks like a woman's, as he traced an idle scrawl in the sand.

The silence was broken only by the crackling of the twigs. Jalona stirred uneasily; he knew that each time he mentioned his bull, his companions seethed with jealousy; yet, because the tongue speaks involuntarily the thoughts most constant in the brain, the love most dominant in the breast of arrogant youth, he could never refrain from mentioning his bull when he spoke.

Sori, the sullen, evil-eyed Mandingo, clenched his right hand slowly till the muscles stood out like corded whips; his eyes filled with blood; he could almost feel Jalona's throat under the pressure of his hand.

Musa, woolly-headed and thick set, grinned broadly, showing his strong white teeth, and his black eyes gleamed with merriment. His high cheekbones and prominent lips indicated his pure Negro blood.

'Truly, he has a right to be proud of his Shadow of Darkness. Were it mine, the earth itself would be too small for me to sit on.' He poked the embers vigorously and did not see the gleam of gratitude Jalona gave him.

'Yes! But Shadow of Darkness is not the only bull in the world. My Brown Laddie is as good a bull any day; broader at chest and larger in the hams.'

'But it's a camel-cow, it's got a hump,' cut in Boma, the

Wangara. He had turned cattle thief through sheer mischief, not necessity.

'Every cow has a hump, you fool. Bring your little measly cow out. Let me see if it hasn't,' he challenged.

'Now, children, children, don't squabble,' quavered the oldest hustler of the gang. 'Do you want the patrol to get us, so that we crawl to prison with broken heads, whilst our cows and sheep fill their bellies?'

The words were scarcely out of his mouth when Musa, who had stretched his cramped limbs, started with a little cry of fear. With outstretched arm, he pointed straight in front of him. All of them scrambled to their feet, except the old man who carefully extinguished the fire, and taking out a knife began to cover up all traces of it.

'Perhaps it is only bush meat moving,' whispered Jalona, contemptuously.

'No, I distinctly saw the gleam of brass buttons. They are coming! The patrol has spotted us!' They quickly cast lots as to who should go on with the cattle.

'Each man one bundle,' warned the old Pa. 'And one drink of water.' They snatched up the bundles and then there was silence. Like one man, they sank flat on their stomachs and began crawling along towards their different animals, each with its own call upon his lips. The main thing was to collect them silently, and drive them on ahead with one man, then run for it.

Jalona's heart thumped against his ribs as he crawled along. He had refused to tether Shadow of Darkness. He had always given him more freedom than the others accorded to theirs. He went back to their last drinking place. If he could reach his bull before the patrol startled him they would all be safe; but if once he gave vent to his terrible roar, all the rest of the cattle would stampede with him.

'Shadow of Darkness,' called Jalona clearly. 'Come, I am calling!'

The beautiful bull raised his head quickly, his whole frame quivering in ecstasy, whilst gracefully and quickly he trotted up the river bank, his coat dripping with water; two heifers who had followed him ambled in his wake.

Jalona saw him start at a quick pace, moving through the mango trees. He gasped with relief. But a moment later cold fear crept up his spine, as the bull, scenting the wind, hesitated, threw back his head and stood still in perplexed uncertainty.

He was too far away to catch his master's scent, for the wind was blowing towards the patrol, and he had lost the direction of his master's voice.

The sweat broke out in little beads on Jalona's forehead. The air was so still that even his first call had echoed and re-echoed. Now that the pursuing party were nearer he dare not call again. They would head straight for the camp. They would catch Shadow of Darkness or startle him into a full gallop towards the camp. They would be shot down like squirrels. The minutes crawled by like hours as he wriggled stealthily onwards, with nothing but grass around him, so that he dare not break cover until the mangoes were reached. He became frantic.

Suddenly he lost his head and jumped up, cupping his mouth with both hands.

'This way, men,' motioned the captain of the patrol about half a mile off. 'We've got them trapped.'

'Shadow!' Jalona never finished the sentence, for a hand was clapped over his mouth.

'You fool!'

His nostrils reeked with the smell of Sori's stale garments as they went down together.

'We want to live, if you don't, damn you. All the others have gone—Musa is on ahead with the cattle. You must leave Shadow of Darkness behind.'

Only the last phrase filtered into Jalona's half-stunned mind. 'Never,' he resolved.

He lay quite still under his enemy, concentrating mind and strength, for now he realized that Sori's grip meant murder. He had no intention of Jalona regaining his bull, or living to tell how he had been maliciously cheated of him—especially now that chance had given him an opportunity of feeling the long, slim throat beneath his fingers. A little more pressure—slowly—slowly, and then . . .

There was a sudden convulsion beneath him and the limp brown body became quite suddenly a wriggling venomous mass, also striking to kill.

The surprise threw Sori off his guard and the two were rolling over and over, first one on top, then the other, each persistently seeking the other's throat.

Jalona felt his strength oozing; though he was a healthy lad, he was no match for a seasoned wrestler of thirty, out to kill.

His breath came in agonizing gasps, jerked out of his body again and again by the huge pounding blows that fell mercilessly like a flail all over his lacerated limbs.

'Shadow of Darkness,' he shrieked in agony. Gradually his grip became loose. A ton of lumbering brute force was pounding its way towards the two fighters.

A low bellow rumbled in its throat. Shadow of Darkness had found his master.

Sori fought and tore at the light brown hands that clung with the last tenacity that comes before unconsciousness.

The furious bull reared its head for a charge. There was a piercing scream; the patrol men stopped in their tracks as a gibbering man was tossed out of the grass in a heap into their ranks.

'Handcuff him, you two, and keep guard.' The others advanced.

Shadow of Darkness licked his master's face and hands, but he did not move. He lowed piteously, but Jalona failed to respond.

Suddenly he became aware of thudding feet, and instinct warned him of danger; yet he deliberately lumbered in the opposite direction and broke into the clearing.

With a shout the patrol men were after him; bullets whizzed about.

'Don't shoot, you fools.' A bullet grazed his side. He roared in anger and turned suddenly. 'He's a beauty. Get him alive. Rope him, you six, the others forward—find the thieves!'

One man was gored to death, two badly wounded and three of the six were hurt before Shadow of Darkness was finally captured. The rest of the patrol men passed within a few inches of Jalona. But being unconscious, he made no sound or movement, and so remained undiscovered.

'But what made you think of coming back?' asked Jalona for the seventh time. He was propped up inside a native hut, his head and side bandaged and a coal pot burning beside him.

'We heard the shouts on Vulture Ridge,' said Musa. 'Pa began to count us. Sori and you were missing.'

'"Sounds as if they have got 'em," mumbled Pa, casually. "Of course, it is a life and death game. Sorry about the lad, though, he is a nice little chap. Of course, you know the hustler law—every one for himself and God for us all—except when we cast lots."'

'I made up my mind then to return and search for you. You were pretty well messed up, but I found you just in time.'

'Is Sori alive?'

'Yes, but I'm not sure how long his sentence is. He is in prison.'

'Shadow of Darkness?' Jalona's voice trembled. Weakly, be brushed away the tears that had filled his eyes.

'He is safe. I think he is in their patrol pen. The white heads intend to keep him and cross breed him. So he is quite safe.'

'Could we catch up the rest of the party, Musa?'

'Well—er—do we want to?'

Both pondered over that point; and suddenly burst out laughing when they found that neither of them wished to.

'When I am well—we will recover Shadow of Darkness. Then, Musa, I am wondering whether I should give him to you.'

'Don't be a fool, Jalona, he's worth a thousand. There are some things I would like to know, though. Where he came from and how you got him?'

'Fiction and truth are equally mixed in his history,' Jalona began. 'He is of a sacred line from Egypt, by the waters of the Nile. Bata, our father, gave his ancestor to the Priest of Osiris and was rewarded with gifts of gold. His calf, a beautiful black and white heifer, guarded and matured by my very great grandparents, was mated with an all-black bull, and again the young bull was as his grandfather, with a white star on his forehead, the eagle on his back and the hump of a beetle under his tongue.

'So the centuries waned and passed until the Fullahs wandered down that way and the Egyptian dynasty crumpled. A big chief took to him the bull worship also; so thus the sacred breed was preserved. My grandfather was a rich cattle owner, and sold all when he got into debt, except the mother of Shadow of Darkness, an all-black heifer. My father inherited her, and as my mother died at my birth and I had no brothers or sisters, my father bequeathed her to me. Shadow of Darkness was born shortly afterwards. He is my only possession, and I named him Shadow of Darkness, for the day after he was born my father was killed in a skirmish. He was with me in my darkest hours, and he shadowed and followed me about like a child. I fed him with my own hand. Now I intend to take him to the West Coast because I can never part from him.'

'Seen the bull we caught the other day, Frank?' queried a young officer of the French patrol at mess.

'No, worth looking at?'

'Perfect beauty! Haven't seen anything like it; jet black pelt, perfect head and horns; such breadth across the shoulders; I don't know how he got here at all.'

'Come outside, Massa! Sentry want you!' a steward whispered.

Together the two friends rose and went out towards the cattle. A terrible lowing rent the air. There was a squealing of pigs and the hens were cackling excitedly. The dogs barked and altogether there was a regular pandemonium.

'What the hell is it about, Momodu?'

'That bull we caught last week go crazy, sir.'

Above the noise rose a clear, sad, sweet tenor.

> 'Shadow of Darkness, listen I am calling.
> Night comes upon us, heavy dew is falling.
> You are powerful as the night!'

With a terrific bellow, the black bull made another charge forward in an effort to burst his halter.

> 'Your breath is sweet as the earth.
> Your eye more gentle than a woman's.
> Your horn, the curved bows of two moons.'

Wonderfully sweet and clear, and infinitely sad, rose Jalona's voice.
'I think we'd better shoot him, or get him into a pen by himself,' suggested the French officer. He began to issue commands to this effect, but the soldiers hung back afraid.

> 'On your forehead is the star of morning,
> On your back the eagle;
> Under your tongue the hump of a beetle,
> Beautiful bull from the line of Osiris.'

Once again Shadow of Darkness charged; this time his halter snapped like thread, and he began pacing round the enclosure, the other cattle rushing away from him.

> 'Your feet are beautiful in strength,
> Your voice is deep as the thunder.'

High and plaintive, pleading and tender, vibrant with emotion, rose and fell the wailing chant of Jalona.

> 'Listen I am calling, calling, calling.
> Oh I need you; I am lonely.
> Come to me quickly—Shadow of Darkness.'

With an answering bellow, the bull cleared the five-foot pen and galloped into the darkness.
'Well I never!' gasped the officer.
By dawn, Musa, Jalona and Shadow of Darkness were far away, hiding in safety.

Talk

A Tale told by an Ashanti of the Gold Coast
to Harold Courlander

ONCE, not far from the city of Accra on the Gulf of Guinea, a country man went out to his garden to dig up some yams to take to market. While he was digging, one of the yams said to him :

'Well, at last you're here. You never weeded me, but now you come around with your digging stick. Go away and leave me alone!'

The farmer turned around and looked at his cow in amazement. The cow was chewing her cud and looking at him.

'Did you say something?' he asked.

The cow kept on chewing and said nothing, but the man's dog spoke up.

'It wasn't the cow who spoke to you,' the dog said. 'It was the yam. The yam says leave him alone.'

The man became angry because his dog had never talked before, and he didn't like his tone, besides. So he took his knife and cut a branch from a palm tree to whip his dog. Just then the palm tree said :

'Put that branch down!'

The man was getting very upset about the way things were going, and he started to throw the palm branch away, but the palm branch said :

'Man, put me down softly!'

He put the branch down gently on a stone, and the stone said :

'Hey, take that thing off me.'

This was enough, and the frightened farmer started to run for his village. On the way he met a fisherman going the other way with a fish trap on his head.

'What's the hurry?' the fisherman asked.

'My yam said, "Leave me alone!" Then the dog said, "Listen to what the yam says!" When I went to whip the dog with a palm branch the tree said, "Put that branch down!" Then the palm branch said, "Do it softly!" Then the stone said, "Take that thing off me!"'

'Is that all?' the man with the fish trap asked. 'Is that so frightening?'

'Well,' the man's fish trap said, 'did he take it off the stone?'

'Wah!' the fisherman shouted. He threw the fish trap on the ground and began to run with the farmer, and on the trail they met a weaver with a bundle of cloth on his head.

'Where are you going in such a rush?' he asked them.

'My yam said, "Leave me alone!"' the farmer said. 'The dog said, "Listen to what the yam says!" The tree said, "Put that branch down!" The branch said, "Do it softly!" And the stone said, "Take that thing off me!"'

'And then,' the fisherman continued, 'the fish trap said, "Did he take it off?"'

'That's nothing to get excited about,' the weaver said, 'no reason at all.'

'Oh yes it is,' his bundle of cloth said. 'If it happened to you you'd run too!'

'Wah!' the weaver shouted. He threw his bundle on the trail and started running with the other men.

They came panting to the ford in the river and found a man bathing.

'Are you chasing a gazelle?' he asked them.

The first man said breathlessly:

'My yam talked to me, and it said, "Leave me alone!" And my dog said, "Listen to your yam!" And when I cut myself a branch the tree said, "Put that branch down!" And the branch said, "Do it softly!" And the stone said, "Take that thing off me!"'

The fisherman panted:

'And my trap said, "Did he?"'

The weaver wheezed:

'And my bundle of cloth said, "You'd run too!"'

'Is that why you're running?' the man in the river asked.

'Well, wouldn't you run if you were in their position?' the river said.

The man jumped out of the water and began to run with the others. They ran down the main street of the village to the house of the chief. The chief's servants brought his stool out, and he came and sat on it to listen to their complaints. The men began to recite their troubles.

'I went out to my garden to dig yams,' the farmer said, waving his arms. 'Then everything began to talk! My yam said, "Leave me alone!" My dog said, "Pay attention to your yam!" The tree said, "Put that branch down!" The branch said, "Do it softly!" And the stone said, "Take it off me!"'

141

'And my fish trap said, "Well, did he take it off?"' the fisherman said.

'And my cloth said, "You'd run too!"' the weaver said.

'And the river said the same,' the bather said hoarsely, his eyes bulging.

The chief listened to them patiently, but he couldn't refrain from scowling.

'Now, this is really a wild story,' he said at last. 'You'd better all go back to your work before I punish you for disturbing the peace.'

So the men went away, and the chief shook his head and mumbled to himself, 'Nonsense like that upsets the community.'

'Fantastic, isn't it?' his stool said. 'Imagine, a talking yam!'

My First Wedding Day in the Bush of Ghosts

AMOS TUTUOLA

Editor's note: The teller of this story, a young boy, has wandered into the heart of the deep forests of West Africa and found himself in a world of ghosts. He struggles to find his way back to mortal habitation and has many fearful adventures on the way. He comes at last to the 8th town of ghosts and there he marries a beautiful young ghostess.

BEFORE the wedding day was reached my friend had chosen one of the most fearful ghosts for me as my 'best man' who was always speaking evil words, even he was punished in the fire of hell more than fifty years for these evil talks and cruelties, but was still growing rapidly in bad habits, then he was expelled from hell to the 'Bush of Ghosts' to remain there until the judgment day as he was unable to change his evil habits at all. When the wedding day arrived all the ghosts and ghostesses of this town, together with the father of the lady whom I wanted to marry, my friend and his mother, my best man and myself went to the church at about ten o'clock, but it was the ghosts' clock said so. When we reached their church I saw that the Reverend who preached or performed the wedding ceremony was the 'Devil.' But as he was preaching he reached the point that I should tell them my name which is an earthly person's name and when they heard the name the whole of them in that church exclaimed at the same time . . . 'Ah! you will be baptized in this church again before you will marry this lady.'

When I heard so from them I agreed, not knowing that Revd. Devil was going to baptize me with fire and hot water as they were baptizing for themselves there. When I was baptized on that day, I was crying loudly so that a person who is at a distance of two miles would not listen before hearing my voice, and within a few minutes every part of my body was scratched by this hot water and fire, but before Revd. Devil could finish the baptism I regretted it. Then I told him to let me go away from their church and I do not want to marry again because I could not bear to be baptized with fire and hot water any longer, but when all of them heard so, they shouted, 'Since you have entered this church you are to be baptized with fire and hot water before you will go out of the church, willing or not you ought to wait and complete the baptism.' But when I heard so from them again, I exclaimed with a terrible voice that . . . 'I will die in their church.' So all of them exclaimed again that . . . 'you may die if you like, nobody knows you here.'

But as ghosts do not know the place or time which is possible to ask questions, so at this stage one of them got up from the seat and asked me . . . 'By the way, how did you manage to enter into the "Bush of Ghosts," the bush which is on the second side of the world between the heaven and earth and which is strictly banned to every earthly person to be entered, and again you have the privilege to marry in this bush as well?' So as these ghosts have no arrangements for anything at the right time and right place, then I answered that I was too young to know which is 'bad' and 'good' before I mistakenly entered this bush and since that time or year I am trying my best to find out the right way back to my home town until I reached the town of 'burglary-ghosts' from where I came with my friend to this town. After I explained as above, then the questioner stood up again and asked me whether I could show them my friend whom I followed to that town. Of course as my friend was faithful, before I could say anything, he and his mother whom we came to visit got up at the same time and said that I am living with a burglar-ghost in the town of the burglar-ghosts. But when my friend and his mother confirmed all that I said and as all the rest of the ghosts are respecting all the burglar-ghosts most because they were supplying them the earthly properties, so they overlooked my offence, then Revd. Devil continued the baptism with hot water and fire.

After the baptism, then the same Revd. Devil preached again for a few minutes, while 'Traitor' read the lesson. All the members of

this church were 'evil-doers.' They sang the song of evils with evils'
melodious tune, then 'Judas' closed the service.

Even 'Evil of evils,' who was the ruler of all the evils, and who
was always seeking evils about, evil-joking, evil-walking, evil-
playing, evil-laughing, evil-talking, evil-dressing, evil-moving, wor-
shipping evils in the church of evils and living in the evil-house
with his evil family, everything he does is evil, attended the service
too, but he was late before he arrived and when he shook hands
with me on that day, I was shocked as if I touch a 'live electric
wire,' but my friend was signalling to me with his eyes not to shake
hands with him to avoid the shock but I did not understand.

Having finished the marriage service, all of us went to my in-laws'
house where everybody was served with a variety of food and all
kinds of ghosts' drinks. After that all the ghost and ghostess dancers
started to dance. Also all the terrible-creatures sent their representatives as 'Skulls,' 'Long-white creatures,' 'Invincible and invisible
Pawn' or 'Give and take' who fought and won the Red people in
the Red-town for the 'Palm-Wine drinker,' 'Mountain-creatures,'
'Spirit of prey' whose eyes flood of light suffocated Palm-Wine
Drinker's wife and also the 'hungry-creature' who swallowed Palm-
Wine Drinker together with his wife when returning from Deads'-
town came and saluted my wife's father and they were served
immediately they arrived. But at last 'Skull' who came from 'Skull
family's town' reported 'Spirit of prey' to my wife's father who
was chief secretary to all the terrible and curious creatures in all
dangerous bushes, that the spirit of prey stole his meat which the
skull put at the edge of the plate in which both were eating as both
were served together with one plate, because plates were not
sufficient to serve each of them with a plate. But before my wife's
father who was their chief secretary could have a chance to come
and settle the matter for them, both of them started to fight fiercely
so that all the ghosts and all the other representatives came nearer
and surrounded them, clapping hands on them in such a way that
if one of these fighters surrenders or gives up it would be very
shameful to him.

Some of these scene-lookers were clapping, and an old Ape, who
was a slave and inherited by my wife's father from his first generation since uncountable years, was beating a big tree under which
both these terrible creatures were fighting as a drum which had a
very large sound. But as this old slave ape was beating the tree as
a drum in such a way that all the scene-lookers who stood round
them could not bear the lofty sound of the tree which was beaten
as a drum and wait or stand still in one place, so all the ghosts,
evils, terrible creatures, my friend, my wife and her father and

myself started to dance at the same time. But as I was intoxicated by the strong drinks which I drank on that day, so I mistakenly smashed a small ghost to death who came from the '9th town of ghosts' to enjoy the merriment of the marriage with us as I was staggering about.

At last I was summoned to the court of evil for wilfully killing a small ghost, but as a little mistake is a serious offence as well as big offence in the 'Bush of Ghosts,' so the 'Evil judge' judged the case at one o'clock of the judgment day and luckily I was freed by a kind lawyer whose mother was the native of the 'Bottomless Ravine's town,' the town which belongs to only 'triplet ghosts and ghostesses.' But if it was not for this incognito lawyer who was very kind to me without knowing him elsewhere I would be imprisoned for fifty years as this is the shortest years for a slightest offence.

After I freed the case then I returned to my in-laws' town and lived there with my wife for a period of about three months and some days before I remembered my mother and brother again, because I did not remember them again when I married the lady. So one morning, I told the father of my wife that I want to leave his town for another one, but I did not tell him frankly that I want to continue to find the way to my home town which I left since I was seven years old. So I told him that I should leave with his daughter who was my wife, he allowed me to go or to leave, but disallowed his daughter to go with me. Of course, when I thought over within myself that however an earthly person might love ghosts, ghosts could not like him heartily in any respect, then I alone left his town in the evening after I went round the town and bade good-bye to the prominent ghosts.

The Lonely Soul

R. E. G. ARMATTOE

I met an old woman
Talking by herself
Down a lonely road.
Talking to herself,
Laughing all the time,
Talking to herself
Down a country road.
Child, you cannot know
Why folks talk alone.
If the road be long
And travellers none,
A man talks to himself.
If showers of sorrows
Fall down like arrows
The lone wayfarer
May talk by himself.
So an old woman
On lone country roads,
Laughing all the time,
May babble to herself
To keep the tears away.
Woman, you are sad!
'Tis the same with me.

There's Always a Way Out

GBEMI

FASASI always knew all the answers. Before his retirement, he had been head messenger at an enormous multiple shop in town and now that he was a settled farmer at remote Ologede, his authority on practically all subjects was upheld without question by his fellow farmers. Ologede was the centre of a large farming area; and in the evening when the men came home, dumped their hoes and cutlasses, and gathered round for a game of *ayo* or a friendly chat over their gourds of palm wine Fasasi's mud hut was always packed full: and he could be observed till well into the night flinging his arms in all directions as he thundered his pronouncement on this subject or that, or regaled his credulous listeners with tales of 'when I was in town.' It came therefore as something of a shock when it became known that Fasasi had been offered a chieftaincy by the *Bale,* but that he was declining it, with thanks. Everyone knew what that meant. A chieftaincy did not fall into everybody's lap, and men have been known to trample on each other's necks without scruple in their bid to win the coveted title. It was also a well-known fact that a title was never won without a generous distribution of money in the right quarters.

The rumour spread—and when Fasasi's friends could no longer pretend to be ignorant of it, they furtively tackled him on the subject one night. 'Tell me, Chief,' asked a man who had been drinking hard all evening, 'you are not really turning down a chieftaincy? It is common talk in the village, you know.'

Fasasi nearly choked over his mug of palm wine, but he knew he must face this sooner or later. 'He-he-he!' he chuckled, and the laughter rang false even in his own ears. 'Fools will prate about what the great do.' This ill-quoted reply was received with silence and a fleeting exchange of looks, and for once Fasasi knew he was losing. 'Ah well,' he continued, 'it is true I have been offered a chieftaincy—the *Asunpewa* "as befits an illustrious son who has been adding to our glory abroad," to quote the *Bale,* the supreme head of Ologede. It is such a great honour—I do feel overwhelmed.'

Whether or not he was turning down the title he would not say : and his friends who knew that he was not a man to let go any chances of bolstering up his vanity, ignored the evasion to save him further embarrassment—if he had the money, they argued, he would not hesitate to accept the title. After all, he had always been anything but displeased when he was addressed as 'chief.' What could be more flattering to him than to wake up and find himself really a chief in his own right—he, the *Asunpewa?*

One by one, they drained their bowls of palm wine and took their leave of him. Fasasi sank in great relief into his favourite armchair. He sat deep in thought for a minute or two and then bawled out, 'Abike! Abike, come here, will you?'

Presently a dark matronly woman sauntered into the room, smiled coyly as she fastidiously tied and retied her *lapa,* and finally knelt down on one knee at Fasasi's feet.

'Abike, my love, I am in a great fix. I need your help.'

Abike heaved a sigh—she knew what was coming.

'You know I am being offered the title of *Asunpewa* . . . .'

'You are? My lord has not told me about this great honour. You certainly deserve it.' Of course she had heard of it—she had had a counter at the *elubo* [1] market, and these last few days the market had talked of nothing else. How thankful she now felt that she had had enough foresight to gather all her savings into safety—her husband would be needing some money, no doubt.

'Pull up a chair and sit down, Abike ; and stop pretending. You know as much as anyone else in this chatty little village of ours. The *Bale* wants to confer the title of *Asunpewa* on me ; but I have not given him an answer one way or the other. You see, I haven't a penny to maintain the proper dignities of the office.' Abike sighed once more—she could see them living on credit and on her market earnings from now on ; and when that was finished, her nest-egg would have to come out. . . . 'We must act and act at once. Somehow the money must be found ! What do you suggest?'

Abike could not immediately think of a way out ; but since she now saw that he knew nothing of her savings and they were not threatened yet, she made up her mind to help her husband.

That night Fasasi slept well in spite of his worries. But his wife spent a sleepless night tossing about her bed of woven rushes, worrying her weary mind for a clue.

By daybreak Abike's efforts had been rewarded. Leaving her little maid to get breakfast ready, she burst into her husband's room and threw open the windows. 'Ah, good morning, my master ; I have been thinking all night : you hardly know how rich you are.'

[1] Yam flour.

Fasasi sat up straight in bed and scratched his head. 'I am talking of your children—six in all you have, haven't you?'

'Yes, but of what use are they? The two little boys are still at school and the girls would not lift a finger to help. Instead of trading or helping me with our products on the farm, they are running around domestic science centres, pretending to learn heaven knows what! A pretty penny they are costing me as it is!' he grumbled.

'You are their father all the same; and I dare say they would do as you wish.' Abike was usually unwilling to mention her husband's children as she was herself childless. Yet now she was out to help him. 'In any case, they wouldn't get married without your consent, would they? If they did, they would be making themselves cheap, like common street-girls.'

Now light began to dawn at last. Following her trend of thought, Fasasi got up and strolled to the window with a distant look in his eye. 'We shall bring the girls home—they will make pretty wives for some lucky fellows! And bring their poor father a handsome dowry into the bargain,' Fasasi added, beaming all over his face and rubbing his hands together in ecstasy. Together they sat down and planned how they would bring the four girls home and land the fortune that was usually a father's consolation for the loss of his daughters.

At market that day, Abike saw to it that the entire village of Ologede prepared their minds for the arrival of her step-daughters.

News soon spreads in small places. At evening, the market broke up and the women carried the news to their little homes. In a day or two, every one knew that Fasasi's four daughters were coming home to get married, and much more besides. Indeed, some people knew to whom they were getting married—which was more than Fasasi and Abike knew, for that was part of their great plan. The truth was that, by creating an interest in their girls, they hoped thereby to be able to raise offers for their hands in marriage. They knew their people well!

And they were right. After a lull for a day or two, Fasasi's house became reasonably full again. Palm wine was handed round and the gathering soon became bright and merry. His friends were unusually witty to-night, bringing out joke after joke that rocked the house with laughter; but though Fasasi joined in the merriment, he kept a watchful eye. At length, the merrymakers prepared to leave, but three of them hung back—they had something important to discuss with their host, they each said.

Fasasi was amused by the coincidence that brought him three different important consultations that night and so prepared was he for what was coming that he simply smiled when, in the secrecy of his bedroom, the first man unburdened his mind. 'Oh yes, you may laugh!' protested the suitor, 'but you just put yourself in my position for a minute. Though I do not want to sing my own praises, I cannot help reminding you of my achievements—head of our local school, with very good prospects of being voted into the local council. Salary—good; state—single; looks—very good.'

Fasasi looked at this man of forty-odd who still preened himself like a young lad of twenty. Ah, well, he thought, there is something in the old turkey anyway and with his pretensions and craving for public approval, he is not likely to ill-treat the poor child. But his voice was full of agony as he replied, 'My dear friend, if I had any idea of your intentions—if I thought the prospect of a union with my poor family would attract you. . . . But the girls are all engaged : I wish I had known.'

'Is there no remedy? Not even if I gave you £30 for her dowry? I have the money on me.'

This was too much for Fasasi : he could sing for joy. Still, it would not do to appear too eager and it was with great reluctance that he finally accepted the money and agreed to break his daughter's previous engagement—an engagement that never existed !

The second man came in, then the third.

Each time it was exactly the same story. They both had their money ready, too. One had forty pounds, the other twenty-five. Evidently, literate educated girls were in great demand and already there was keen competition for Fasasi's children. An aged man wanted a wife with just these qualifications for his son who was training as a surveyor and he was gratified to find her in 'such a commendable home.'

Fasasi listened to him with an indifference he certainly did not feel. How it tickled his vanity to find himself father-in-law to both a headmaster and a surveyor, all overnight, as it were ! And the princely sum of £70 was his already ! Shrewd business man that he was, he could not help surmising that prices might soar higher later on and so, when the last man approached him, he quite gently but firmly put his foot down. 'I am so very sorry,' he said, 'I wish you had told me earlier. As it is, it is all settled. The girls are all given away.'

When he had locked the door on the last of his friends, Fasasi ran back into his sitting-room and shouted to his wife, who, however, was now sitting there in his favourite armchair, a mischievous smile on her lips. 'Guess what?' he said, looking mysterious.

'You've got £70 in your pocket,' she replied promptly and then, unashamed, she added by way of explanation, 'I was just outside your window all the time. Congratulations!'

'Here, you take this pound, I owe it all to your genius really. Well, to-morrow you shall go down to town and bring back all four of those pretty girls of mine. By Jove, I never knew how rich I was, did I now?' He was so obviously happy, so pleased with himself.

Abike folded up her pound, mentally saving it up to augment her *elubo* trade.

'Ah, isn't it just too good to be true? I—ex-head messenger and farmer: I, the *Asunpewa!*' And with that he heaved up the ample sleeves of his *agbada* and waved an imaginary horse-tail for the benefit of an equally imaginary audience as he strutted up and down the whole length of his sitting-room . . . all to the amusement of his wife, who was herself already seeing visions.

What a Day!

A traditional West African poem ·
translated from the Yoruba by
E. L. Lasebikan

What a day, when the morning air does not resound with the
    pounding of yams!
What a day when I listened in vain to hear them sift the flour!
When the frying pots do not simmer with the fricassee of rabbits
    and birds.
What a day when the expert wakes up under the shadow of
    starvation!

The Sergeant who Rejoiced in his Youth

M. W. SINAH

ONCE there was a Sergeant who was very handsome and tall and radiant because he had read in the Bible, 'Rejoice O young man, in thy youth,' and he made up his mind to do that.

Well, as every one knows who has been in large cities, it is quite easy to lead a merry, carefree life there, if you make up your mind to do it, so this Sergeant got asked to a lot of parties and dances and moonlight picnics, and really the ladies made a great fuss of him; and during the hot weather he spent his leave at seaside hostels, and could have gone to other distant countries if only the Commanding Officer would give him an extension.

So one day the Adjutant sent for the Sergeant and said, 'Look here, Sergeant, the Colonel has been talking about you, and he says he doesn't like the way you are behaving, and neither do I; so it's about time you chucked it. You must begin to take a little interest in your profession. Get out and have your hair cut, and stop using that filthy coconut oil on it.'

The Sergeant was quite upset because he did not use coconut oil on his hair at all, but another much more expensive preparation of which he was proud; but he was wise enough not to mention that to the Adjutant and said, 'I am sorry, sir. Please put my name down for the next promotion examination.'

The Adjutant was very surprised, but he put his name down for the next examination, and then the Sergeant came back to the Battalion Office and asked the Adjutant what were the best books to read for the promotion, which was a very tactless thing to do, because, of course, the Adjutant did not know and had to tell him to clear out as he was busy.

So the Sergeant was very subdued for a few days, and refused quite a lot of invitations in order to study for his examination, and one evening he went to a lecture on tactics and afterwards he went to the hairdresser's, where he had a hair-cut, a shampoo and then a little face massage, because the barber said his face needed that; he then looked in at the club to see if there were any books on military history in the library he could pick up, but instead of these he picked up a lady called Mrs. Bluebell, who said she liked the smell of his new hair-oil, and he must come home with her to dinner as her husband had gone off on manœuvres and left her all alone.

The Sergeant said he was sorry he could not dine that special night because he was studying history for promotion, and then it turned out that Mrs. Bluebell knew a lot of history because she had been to America, Australia and several other places; so the Sergeant changed his mind and went to dine with her, and she taught him a lot about the Wars of the Roses and Waterloo, and 1066 and all that, and her memory for dates was marvellous, though she completely forgot the one her husband was due home again, and the Sergeant really had a very narrow escape—though, of course, that was a week later when he happened to be dining with her again to study the campaigns of Henry the Eighth.

Well, the Sergeant duly sat for his examination, and I am sorry to say he failed in all the subjects and got no marks for history at all.

So the Adjutant was very angry and sent for the Sergeant and said, 'You are a disgrace to the Regiment and · I hope you are thoroughly ashamed of yourself, and what is more, the entire Battalion is talking about you, because no Warrant Officer has ever been known to fail in all the subjects before, though it's quite a common thing to fail in five out of six. I call your conduct lamentable. Go and get your hair cut and stop using that filthy coconut oil.'

The Sergeant was more depressed than ever because he had just got a new hair-oil from one of the leading firms in Calcutta, which was very expensive. But he went to the barber's and got a hair cut, had a shampoo and face massage, and then the barber curled up the ends of his moustache with a hot iron, which made him look very dashing. Then off to the club again to look up an advertisement he had seen in some papers about a correspondence course in military subjects, which he thought he might join, but instead he joined Mrs. Snowdrop, who happened to be sitting in the lounge. 'You are looking very well, and I like your moustache very much,' she said, 'and the smell of that hair-oil is really delicious; come along and have dinner with me to-night, because Mr. Snowdrop is in hospital with a sprained knee.'

The Sergeant wanted very much to go to dinner with Mrs. Snowdrop because she was very smart and very pretty, and he knew she would give him a much better dinner than he would get at the Mess and perhaps a glass of wine with it; but he remembered just in time about the disgrace he was in for failing in all the subjects of his examination and said, 'No, I am very sorry I cannot dine with you, because I am going to take a correspondence course in geography.'

And Mrs. Snowdrop said, 'Oh, that's quite easy. I know a lot of geography; we can talk the subject over first and then you can correspond with me about it afterwards.'

So the Sergeant went to dine with Mrs. Snowdrop, and after dinner she taught him that Aden was famous for ostrich feathers and coral necklaces, and that Port Said was renowned for picture postcards and that lawyers and judges came from Allahabad: and then the Sergeant went home and corresponded with her a lot about these and other things until Mr. Snowdrop came home from hospital and read one of the letters: and for some reason he kicked up hell about it, and said the correspondence course must stop or he would see his solicitors and have the Sergeant tried by court martial.

And the Sergeant had to sit for his examination again without any preparation, and he failed in all the subjects.

Well, this time the Commanding Officer sent for the Sergeant, and at first he was inclined to be very angry: and he saw that the Sergeant, instead of being his usual gay and radiant self, was looking very sorrowful and depressed. The Commanding Officer thought that perhaps he was sick or something, so he said in quite a kindly voice, 'What is the trouble, my boy? Is there anything on your mind?'

So the Sergeant looked at the Commanding Officer with a very grateful expression and said, 'Yes, sir, there is. Every time I try to pass my examinations I seem to get mixed up with women in some sort of way. In fact, in everything I do I seem to get mixed up with women, which makes it very difficult to concentrate, because as you know, sir, they are very charming creatures and really a full-time job in themselves.'

And the Commanding Officer sighed heavily and looked very thoughtful and then said, 'Yes, what you say is true. They are always charming and always a full-time job, and I found it so when I was young. Looking back on those days with regret, I now find I did not make the best use of my opportunities.'

Well, the Sergeant sighed heavily, too, to show how much he sympathized with his superior officer, and then he said that he would try to do better and would really work harder for the next examination; but the Commanding Officer jumped up from his chair and put a friendly hand on his shoulder and said, 'No, don't do that. There is plenty of time; forget about examinations and continue to enjoy yourself when you are still young.'

So the Sergeant continued to rejoice in his youth and everybody was very pleased—particularly Mrs. Snowdrop, whose husband was again in bed with the same sprained knee.

O Blue-Sky Duchess![1]

THOMAS A. CODJOE

🏵

O LADY of Blue-Sky Fashion and Twenty plus Six Alphabetical Spells of adorable beauty, you were here at a time when the Star Lennox-Boyd had succeeded in destroying the plans of a Communist Worshipper of evil spirits. Let us pray in Eloii, Eloiyah-Jesu-Aggrey Alpha et Omega, and leap we shall leap to a blessed Paradise after the resignation of Nkrumah's woeful Government. O Duchess, Duchess of Kent, take my wings (the thirteenth soul in me) and plough the waves in the universe with me to a kingdom where the Sun is Adam acknowledgeable in the traditional sisterhood of infallible angels as the children of God.

I have a message for the British Throne, in a line or two, the constitutional white paper is good to fit no gamblers of democracy but it fits an Empire of Royal Christian Citizenship and to Queen Elizabeth II, the House of Commons and the Temple of the Lords, I post boundless thankfulness per the Duchess of Kent, Duchess, O my lustre Duchess, we shall travel with the space-time of snails in the angels' arts and by thine convocational rape of the throat of six winds shall a Ghanaian graduate in the astral elevation of the heavenly bodies, lit those who fish wisdom to my height of the twelfth hour (mensa, a table of the Star Jesus) should fail except they are enemies to the soul of Judas Iscarus and his communist fellowship. It is now time to address a divinely inspired welcome to the Matron of Kent with all the flappings in the wings of the Queen's Day Star, styled in classical tales as the oldest of all Lawyers and Philosophers; point 1, are the Queen's preservation of law all correct in Ghana via Jibowu lex? we say yes not in Kwame Nkrumah but in a Lennox-Boyd, exception in the law is

[1] A 1d. pamphlet written to welcome the Duchess of Kent to the Ghana Independence celebrations.

cast with hopes of the Eagle Codjoe whose dominant history the dupe was about to excavate by neopaganism plans and vindictives, flee, he flees, this is my cap it does not fit a graduate with waxen wings, read our identification passport in the Commissioner of Police Record Book that no man can take the name of the Lord in vain, Jesus made wine with Akpeteshie to tell history that the man who spoke of Saltpond as his holy city is fraudulent, lex Jupiter circulavit Ghana et England Universitas Duchess Kent umbra Jesu-Codjoe Pater Africa convocat Legon, Nkrumah Kwame nil ambulans Buckingham Castra London fiat, ago jusjurandum Dii Caeli me.

We are here to speak to the Duchess of Kent by natural wireless, viz :—phona Duch Kent aeroplans hiac Jesu cogno, take my warm and royal greetings in this writing to signify a wish I have in me to be present at the air port to swinton one sweet smile to Thine Dear Spirit in which I shall for ever worship with dozens of cares flowing from a bond signed by the Prince of Divinities and sealed in the Gods of no Nkrumah's chronology fiat. Thine, O Thine, my Brave Duchess, is the shield in Dii, forsake the doleful feelings in Thine Heart for the Duke is the Soul in Thine Profortunate Late Husband; in the professional wisdom in which I live as Heavenly Duke and the Father of All Angels, it is written, if the flesh is the man in an Aggrey of Africa, there shall be no resurrection of dead christians, Thine Royal Companion flies away to join the blessed Singing Stars, take my wedding ring from Miss Jessey May Mankee of Maidstone, Kent and live with me in Jesu.

I need to be planted in Ghana millions of palm trees, pines, cane-sugar, oranges, melons, grapes, sweet apples, ginger etc. I shall use the Akpeteshie-trade-spirit for the manufacture of gun powder, highly explosive rockets which I call in my parliamentary politics bombs. Recounting the Prime Minister's speech under calligraphology caped in the columns of the *Daily Graphic* of 25/2/1957 at Saltpond, the Premier made the subjunctive reference that they have no bombs but they have brains, O History, History, tell the ass that the Lord Jesus its Rider and Master-Builder of the New World (Heaven) Ghana, said that in his ruling lexicon all those rockets which the Government ordered for the Holy Celebration of Independence in Africa are called representative bombs. Have you brains really O Kwame Nkrumah, how can you and your people tell wise men in Europe and America to believe that you have brains in your heads since they were using refined river muds with the shape and early resemblance of the mud in the Korle Lagoon to manufacture coloured school chalk. Can men with thoughtful brains buy river muds and powder of burnt sea shells etc. with money? If I tell Kwame Nkrumah that he has the golden aged sense how can I have the chance to give him eyes to see, ears to hear, way to know the key of natural fractions of mathematical rudiments in practical chemistry, the scale-drawing equilibrium materialized in shades of the sun per lux radix ars lex ago Jesus Mensa hiac.

The Government of Ghana should note that I have a Queen's Bench Law which I put in verse as follows :—Nearly five years ago I manufactured wine with Akpeteshie at Bukom Square, Accra. As my licence in the Police Record Book had preceded the legalization of the gin *in* parliament, the Government falls under this licence. However, I wish the leaders of the Government to be little consistent in the manner in which they deal with the Chiefs, they read the white paper and to-day, they say we agree, but to-morrow, they lose their mental emotions and take to talk of Brong like hungry and wingless bees which made devastating meal of all the honey they brought forth for the making of cakes and delicious wines, H.M.S. Kushara carries 80 million discoveries, O Duchess of Kent, smiles.

Anansi's Fishing Expedition

A Tale from Ghana

In the country of Ashanti, not far from the edge of the great West African forest, there was a man named Anansi,[1] who was known to all the people for miles around. Anansi was not a great hunter, or a great worker, or a great warrior. His specialty was being clever. He liked to outwit people. He liked to live well, and to have other people do things for him. But because all the people of the country knew about Anansi and had had trouble with him, he had to keep thinking of new ways to get something for nothing.

One day Anansi was sitting in the village when a man named Osansa came along.

'I have an idea,' Anansi said. 'Why don't we go and set fish traps together? Then we shall sell the fish and be quite rich.'

---

[1] Hero of many West African tales, Anansi is sometimes portrayed as a spider and sometimes as a man. He is usually engaged in a battle of wits with his neighbours. Anansi stories have travelled as far as the West Indies.

But Osansa knew Anansi's reputation very well, and so he said :

'No, I have as much food as I can eat or sell. I am rich enough. Why don't you set your fish traps by yourself?'

'Ha! Fish alone? Then I'd have to do all the work!' Anansi said. 'What I need is a fool for a partner.'

Osansa went away, and after a while another man named Anene came along.

'I have an idea,' Anansi said. 'Why don't the two of us go and set fish traps together? Then we shall sell the fish and be quite rich.'

Anene knew Anansi very well too, but he seemed to listen thoughtfully.

'That sounds like a fine idea,' he said. 'Two people can catch more fish than one. Yes, I'll do it.'

The news went rapidly around the village that Anansi and Anene were going on a fishing expedition together. Osansa met Anene in the market and said :

'We hear you are going to trap fish with Anansi. Don't you know he is trying to make a fool of you? He has told every one that he needs a fool to go fishing with him. He wants someone to set the fish traps and do all the work, while he gets all the money for the fish.'

'Don't worry, friend Osansa, I won't be Anansi's fool,' Anene said.

Early the next morning Anansi and Anene went into the woods to cut palm branches to make their fish traps.

Anansi was busy thinking how he could make Anene do most of the work. But when they came to the place where the palm trees grew, Anene said to Anansi :

'Give me the knife, Anansi. I shall cut the branches for the traps. We are partners. We share everything. My part of the work will be to cut branches, your part of the work will be to get tired for me.'

'Just a minute, let me think,' Anansi said. 'Why should I be the one to get tired?'

'Well, when there's work to be done someone must get tired,' Anene said. 'That's the way it is. So if I cut the branches, the least you can do is to get tired for me.'

'Hah, you take me for a fool?' Anansi said. 'Give me the knife. I shall cut the branches and you get tired for me!'

So Anansi took the knife and began cutting the branches from the trees. Every time he chopped, Anene grunted. Anene sat down in the shade and groaned from weariness, while Anansi chopped and hacked and sweated. Finally the wood for the fish traps was cut. Anansi tied it up into a big bundle. Anene got up from the ground, holding his back and moaning.

'Anansi, let me carry the bundle of wood now, and you can get tired for me,' Anene said.

'Oh, no, my friend Anene,' Anansi said, 'I am not that simple-minded. I'll carry the wood myself, and you can take the weariness for me.'

So he hoisted the bundle to the top of his head and the two of them started back to the village. Anene groaned all the way.

'Oh, oh!' he moaned. 'Take it easy, Anansi! Oh, oh!'

When they came to the village Anene said :

'Let me make the fish traps, Anansi, and you just sit down and get tired for me.'

'Oh, no,' Anansi said. 'You just keep on as you are.' And he made the fish traps while Anene lay on his back in the shade with his eyes closed, moaning and groaning.

And while he was making the traps, working in the heat with perspiration running down his face and chest, Anansi looked at Anene lying there taking all his weariness and sore muscles for him, and he shook his head and clucked his tongue.

'Anene thinks he is intelligent,' he said to himself. 'Yet look at him moaning and groaning there, practically dying from weariness!'

When the fish traps were done Anene climbed to his feet and said, 'Anansi, my friend, now let me carry the fish traps to the water, and you can get tired for me.'

'Oh, no,' Anansi said. 'You just come along and do your share. I'll do the carrying, you do the getting tired.'

So they went down to the water, Anansi carrying and Anene moaning. When they arrived, Anene said to Anansi :

'Now wait a minute, Anansi, we ought to think things over here. There are sharks in this water. Someone is apt to get hurt. So let me go in and set the traps, and should a shark bite me, then you can die for me.'

'Wah!' Anansi howled. 'Listen to that! What do you take me for? I'll go in the water and set the traps myself, and if I am bitten, then you can die for me!' So he took the fish traps out into the water and set them and then the two of them went back to the village.

The next morning when they went down to inspect the traps they found just four fish. Anene spoke first.

'Anansi, there are only four fish here. You take them. To-morrow there will probably be more, and then I'll take my turn.'

'Now, what do you take me for?' Anansi said indignantly. 'Do you think I am simple-minded? Oh, no, Anene, you take the four fish and I'll take my turn to-morrow.'

So Anene took the four fish and carried them to town and sold them.

Next day when they came down to the fish traps, Anene said:

'Look, there are only eight fish here. I'm glad it's your turn, because to-morrow there doubtless will be more.'

'Just a minute,' Anansi said. 'You want me to take to-day's fish so that to-morrow you get a bigger catch? Oh, no, these are all yours, partner; to-morrow I'll take my share.'

So Anene took the eight fish and carried them to town and sold them.

Next day when they came to look in the traps they found sixteen fish.

'Anansi,' Anene said, 'take the sixteen fish. Little ones, too. I'll take my turn to-morrow.'

'Of course you'll take your turn to-morrow, it's my turn to-day,' Anansi said. He stopped to think. 'Well, now, you are trying to make a fool out of me again! You want me to take these sixteen miserable little fish so that you can get the big catch to-morrow, don't you? Well, it's a good thing I'm alert! You take the sixteen to-day and I'll take the big catch to-morrow!'

So Anene carried the sixteen fish to the market and sold them.

Next day they came to the traps and took the fish out. But by this time the traps had rotted in the water.

'Well, it's certainly your turn to-day,' Anene said. 'And I'm very glad of that. Look, the fish traps are rotten and worn out. We can't use them any more. I'll tell you what—you take the fish to town and sell them, and I'll take the rotten fish traps and sell them. The fish traps will bring an excellent price. What a wonderful idea!'

'Hm,' Anansi said. 'Just a moment, don't be in such a hurry. I'll take the fish traps and sell them myself. If there's such a good price to be had, why shouldn't I get it instead of you? Oh, no, you take the fish, my friend.'

Anansi hoisted the rotten fish traps up on his head and started off for town. Anene followed him, carrying the fish. When they arrived in the town Anene sold his fish in the market, while Anansi walked back and forth singing loudly:

'I am selling rotten fish traps! I am selling wonderful rotten fish traps!'

But no one wanted rotten fish traps, and the townspeople were angry that Anansi thought they were so stupid they would buy them. All day long Anansi wandered through the town singing:

'Get your rotten fish traps here! I am selling wonderful rotten fish traps!'

Finally the head man of the town heard about the affair. He, too, became very angry, and he sent messengers for Anansi. When they brought Anansi to him he asked indignantly:

'What do you think you are doing, anyway? What kind of nonsense is this you are trying to put over the people of the town?'

'I'm selling rotten fish traps,' Anansi said, 'very excellent rotten fish traps.'

'Now what do you take us for?' the chief of the town said. 'Do you think we are ignorant people? Your friend Anene came and sold good fish, which the people want, but you come trying to sell something that isn't good for anything and just smell the town up with your rotten fish traps. It's an outrage. You insult us.'

The head man turned to the townspeople who stood near by, listening.

'Take him away and whip him,' he said.

The men took Anansi out to the town gate and beat him with sticks. Anansi shouted and yelled and made a great noise. When at last they turned him loose, Anene said to him:

'Anansi, this ought to be a lesson to you. You wanted a fool to go fishing with you, but you didn't have to look so hard to find one. You were a fool yourself.'

Anansi nodded his head.

'Yes,' he said thoughtfully, rubbing his back and his legs where they had beaten him. And he looked reproachfully at Anene. 'But what kind of partner are you? At least you could have taken the pain while I took the beating.'

He who has lost all

DAVID DIOP

Translated from the French by Dorothy Blair

The sun shone brightly in my hut
And my women were fair and pliant
As the palm in the evening breeze.
My children glided through the great river's waters
With its deadly depths
And my canoes struggled with the crocodiles.
The maternal moon accompanied our dances
The frenzied heavy rhythm of the tom-tom,
Tom-tom of joy days, careless of the morrow
   In the midst of the fires of liberty.

Then one day, silence . . .
The rays of the sun seemed to die
In my hut now empty of meaning.
My women crushed their painted mouths
On the thin hard lips of the steel-eyed conquerors
And my children quit their peaceful nakedness
Donning the uniform of iron and bloodshed.
Your voice too had died
The chains of slavery have rent my heart
Tom-toms of night, tom-toms of my fathers.

The Return of the Soldier

FRANCIS OBIKA

 O N the heels of War followed hardship. There were none to work in the farms any more. There were none to clear the roads again. The walls fell and remained fallen. The houses leaked but remained unrepaired. The thatches rotted on the roofs but there was none to renew them. There were no young men to lead the maidens to dances any more. Decay set in in every aspect of life.

Wives were paid allotments for their husbands on active service. They used the money to pay for the food and other services which they could no longer provide for themselves. Some soldiers sent money to their relatives to keep for them till they returned. When the money had grown big, evil thoughts entered the minds of those relatives. They wished the soldiers might die on the battlefields so that they could use the money for themselves. Some even went to native doctors to make charms which could cause the death of a soldier on a battlefield.

Some soldiers did die on battlefields. That was not remarkable, for why else did they go to war but to feed the cannons? Some marched from one battlefield to another with charmed lives. Some were taken prisoners in enemy countries. Some deserted their units and embraced new countries. Some even managed to return to Ojindu after their desertion. Some won distinctions on one battlefield after another. Some were maimed and carried back to Ojindu. Some suffered shell shock and became insane. Those who persevered to the end did not return until the two atom bombs had demolished Hiroshima and Nagasaki.

Then the great homeward march began. They came by giant steamers over endless seas. It took many months, many weeks and many days. The great reunion was marked by happy celebrations. The fatted calf was killed and its blood sprinkled on the shrine of the ancestors. There was so much to tell by those who returned. Those who had imagination painted the pictures with art until those who had not exposed the crude truth. Then the wonder did not last nine days.

Not all the home-comings were happy. There were some tragedies. Some ran amok when they came home to find their trusts betrayed. Some found their wives with children they did not help to bear. Other armies had stayed at Ojindu while they were away. Mankind being the same all the world over, the flesh had overcome the spirit. Some returned to find all kith and kin extinct. There was sorrow and there was joy. Life had to be built afresh. They had received the war gratuity promised by the Government. At first it seemed a good lump of money. But soon they found it could not do everything.

The war veteran looked on the soil. It had grown poor through years of ceaseless cultivation. He thought of the life he had led in the army. Apart from the actual fighting there was plenty to eat. He thought of the countries he had visited. He thought of the new life in foreign lands. Why should be spend his life toiling to no profit? His soul rebelled. He had seen the happier side of life. He wanted to have a share of the good things of life. He turned from the soil, donned the khaki uniform again and went to the cities. From office to office he presented himself. The ex-serviceman became the problem of the day. The Government had promised them employment. Let the Government redeem its promise. The politicians caught the cry of ex-serviceman. The press printed banner headlines in support of the ex-serviceman. There was not enough employment to go round. An opportunity was created for rogues to get rich. Jobbery became the order of the day. Whatever was left of the war gratuity was handed over to the men in the key places in order to get a job no matter what sort. In some cases money could not avail simply because there were no more jobs. In desperation the veteran turned his attention to other sources. But he was determined not to go back to the land.

At first one man went to the cities. Then followed another; and then there was a rush. The temporary rejuvenation of social life in Ojindu created by the arrival of her youths from the wars was gone. This time it was worse because the youths married the maidens and all went away. The hopes of re-establishment of the old order were fast receding. There would never be any more folk dances. Maidens with quivering breasts ripe like mangoes would no more step to the rhythm of the music played on flutes, drums and gongs. The folk tales would no more be told beneath the stars at night, nor the carnivals be held under the moon. What a civilization! What a vengeance!

The Parable of the Eagle

JAMES AGGREY

A CERTAIN man went through a forest seeking any bird of interest he might find. He caught a young eagle, brought it home and put it among his fowls and ducks and turkeys, and gave it chickens' food to eat even though it was an eagle, the king of birds.

Five years later a naturalist came to see him and, after passing through his garden, said : 'That bird is an eagle, not a chicken.'

'Yes,' said its owner, 'but I have trained it to be a chicken. It is no longer an eagle, it is a chicken, even though it measures fifteen feet from tip to tip of its wings.'

'No,' said the naturalist, 'it is an eagle still : it has the heart of an eagle, and I will make it soar high up to the heavens.'

'No,' said the owner, 'it is a chicken, and it will never fly.'

They agreed to test it. The naturalist picked up the eagle, held it up, and said with great intensity : 'Eagle, thou art an eagle ; thou dost belong to the sky and not to this earth ; stretch forth thy wings and fly.'

The eagle turned this way and that, and then, looking down, saw the chickens eating their food, and down he jumped.

The owner said : 'I told you it was a chicken.'

'No,' said the naturalist, 'it is an eagle. Give it another chance to-morrow.'

So the next day he took it to the top of the house and said : 'Eagle, thou art an eagle ; stretch forth thy wings and fly.' But again the eagle, seeing the chickens feeding, jumped down and fed with them.

Then the owner said : 'I told you it was a chicken.'

'No,' asserted the naturalist, 'it is an eagle, and it still has the heart of an eagle ; only give it one more chance, and I will make it fly to-morrow.'

The next morning he rose early and took the eagle outside the city, away from the houses, to the foot of a high mountain. The sun was just rising, gilding the top of the mountain with gold, and every crag was glistening in the joy of that beautiful morning.

He picked up the eagle and said to it : 'Eagle, thou art an eagle ; thou dost belong to the sky and not to this earth ; stretch forth thy wings and fly !'

The eagle looked around and trembled as if new life were coming to it ; but it did not fly. The naturalist then made it look straight at the sun. Suddenly it stretched out its wings and, with the screech of an eagle, it mounted higher and higher and never returned. It was an eagle, though it had been kept and tamed as a chicken !

My people of Africa, we were created in the image of God, but men have made us think that we are chickens, and we still think we are ; but we are eagles. Stretch forth your wings and fly ! Don't be content with the food of chickens !

Congo

LÉOPOLD SÉDAR SENGHOR

Translated from the French by Dorothy Blair

Oho ! Congo oho ! To beat out the rhythm of thy name wide on
    the waters on the rivers on all that remembers
Let me stir up the voice of the *koras*,[1] Koyaté.[2] The ink of the
    scribe grows dim with oblivion.

Oho ! Congo recumbent on thy bed, forest-bed, queen of tamed
    Africa
May phallic mountains bear aloft thy standard
For thou art woman by my head by my tongue, for thou art woman
    by my entrails.
Mother of all nostrilled things, crocodile hippopotamus
Lamentin iguana fishes and birds, mother of flood-waters wet-
    nurse of the harvest
Great woman ! water open wide to the oar and the stem of the
    canoe
Ma Saô my woman with the thighs of violence with long arms
    decked in still water-lilies

[1] A West African string instrument which sounds like a harp.
[2] Name of a poet.

Woman most loved of *ouzougou*,[1] body of incorruptible oil, skin of diamantine night.

Tranquil goddess with the flaccid smile, calm above the giddying turmoil of thy blood
Thou of long lineage malarious, deliver me from the surging of my blood.
Tom-tom thou thou tom-tom of the bounding panther, of the ant strategist
Of the slimy abomination rising on the third day from the *poto-poto*[2] of the marshes
Ha! above all things, from the spongy soil and the smooth songs of the White-man
But deliver me from the joyless night and watch o'er the silent forest.
So let me be the slender standing tree-trunk and the twenty-six cubit leap
In the trade-winds, let me be the flight of the canoe on the smooth shield of thy belly.
Glades of thy bosom islets of love, hills of amber and of *gongo*[3]
Tanns[4] of childhood *tanns* of Joal, and of Dyilôr in September
And night of Asnières in September—in the calm and mildness of the season.
Tranquil flowers of thy hair, petals so white of thy mouth
Above all interchange of soft words at the new moon, until the midnight of the blood.
Deliver me from the night of my blood, for the silence of the forests lies in wait.

My beloved at my side whose eburnean oil bends to her will my hands my heart
My strength exalted in abandon, my honour in submission
And my knowledge in the instinct of thy rhythm. The dance-leader twists in abandon
Foremost of his sex at the sight of the bull, like the Killer-with-the-eyes-of-flame.
Bells beat the rhythm tongues beat the rhythm oars beat the rhythm of the dance of the Master-of-the-oars.
See his canoe! befitting the exulting choruses of Fadyoutt
And I cry out for twice times two hands for the tom-tom, and forty virgins to sing of his exploits.

[1] A tree of hard, black wood.
[2] Mud.
[3] African perfume.
[4] Wide bare stretch of land from where the sea has receded.

Beat the rhythm, glowing arrows, talons of the noon-day sun
Beat the rhythm, cowrie-rattles, of the gushing of the Great-Water
And death on the crest of exultation, at the unchallengeable call
 of the gulf.

But the canoe will arise again through the white foam water-lilies
The pliant bamboo will float again in the transparent morning of
 the world.

The Devil at Yolahun Bridge

ABIOSEH D. NICOL

SANDERSON twirled his fountain-pen slowly round between the
fingers of one hand and drummed with the other on the desk before
him. His eyes wandered to the distant green hills of Kissiland that
marked the boundary between his district and the next. He looked
again at the form in front of him, printed on Crown Agents' paper,
and read it to himself for the tenth time. 'District Officer's Annual
Report West African Colonial Service (Confidential).' The blank
space below looked wider than ever. Since McPherson, his Senior
District Officer, had gone home on leave, he had kept postponing
writing it. He had received a gentle reminder from Headquarters'
Secretariat a few days ago. He felt he really must get down to it
this afternoon.

'Momoh!' he shouted. The young West African clerk came out
of the adjoining office.

'Bring me all the Annual Reports you can lay your hands on.'

'There are about fifty, sir,' Momoh said with some trepidation,
'but I can bring them all if you want them,' he added hastily.

'Bring the past ten years, then.'

When the Reports arrived he glanced through them. He could
not believe that anyone bothered to read them. What would
happen, he wondered, if he sent, say, the 1936 Report verbatim
with the name of a sub-chief altered here and the name of a village
there; or, say, a blank form with some cryptic remark like 'Con-
fidentially (as requested) the Africans have not changed much over

the past year, but my fellow Europeans in the station have altered beyond belief. Pale hesitant inexperience, for example, in many cases has slowly but steadily given way to an incredible sunburnt competence.'

No, wit was not appreciated in high places. Could he start on an historical note? Or on an anthropological one? He decided against that. He had better stick to the familiar essential things instead— new roads, the increase in trade, and the shift of the young from the village to the towns. Now to begin.

'Excuse me, sir, I have not yet read out to you your appointments for the week.' Momoh had appeared through the doorway and was standing in front of his desk.

Sanderson suppressed a cry of impatience as he remembered that he had impressed on the clerk the importance every Monday morning of reminding him of his week's appointments. He could easily look them up himself, but he was trying to train Momoh to a high pitch of secretarial efficiency and, besides, it gave him a secret pleasure to pretend he was a vast administrator with numerous and important appointments. Momoh himself enjoyed the whole business intensely. He was a short, stocky youth with an alert face and boyish enthusiasm. His breast-pocket was always full of finely sharpened pencils and fountain-pens with different coloured ink.

'All right, Mr. Momoh, read them out.'

Momoh cleared his throat and read in a slightly sing-song voice. First, there was the annual inspection of the local secondary school. This was run by a nervous, leathery Irish priest and it had to be inspected every year before receiving the Government grant. The inspection was a formality; for education officers came round from time to time during the year to see that the standards were maintained. Then there was the semi-official engagement, the following night, to lecture to the local African club.

'Will you be there, Mr. Momoh?' Sanderson asked him, and at once regretted doing so lest his clerk should regard it as an official command.

'Oh yes, I shall be there certainly, sir,' Momoh said earnestly. 'Things like that,' he continued, 'contribute to a man's uplift of the mind.'

'Well, I don't think this will,' Sanderson remarked drily. 'Still, continue.' On Thursday there was to be the visit of the P.W.D. Headquarters' engineer. Momoh had put into operation the simple procedure required—the rest-house to be got ready, the file for maintenance and repair of Government buildings to be gone through, and new requirements determined or invented; the

Government lorry to be made ready in case that of the visiting engineer broke down on the way to Kissy or when returning from it. Sanderson looked through the list, initialled his approval, and asked Momoh the name of the engineer.

'Mr. O. E. Hughes, sir,' Momoh replied, with a slight smile which puzzled Sanderson at the time, but which he remembered afterwards. One of our Celtic brethren, Sanderson thought to himself. Aloud he said, 'Right. Thank you very much,' dismissing the clerk.

'Now, about Hughes,' he said, half aloud to himself.

He could not place him; the name did not sound familiar. Must be new, he thought, and decided to look him up in the most recent Senior Staff List. He ran his finger down the column of the Senior P.W.D. Staff until he came to the Hs. Ah, there it was, Hughes, Oluyemi Egbert. Oh, that was it, he was an African. That was why he had never heard of him before. He whistled softly to himself. By Jove, there might be complications. Usually, visiting members of the senior staff were taken to the European Club in the evenings they spent in Kissy. He began to go through the list of members in his mind one by one, trying to picture what their reactions would be to an African guest. Then he wondered for a moment, a little shamefacedly, whether it was not he who had started making excuses and finding reasons before anything happened. But no, he decided, it was his duty to make sure beforehand that there were no incidents, because if there were he would have to make a report and probably bear the unspoken blame from Headquarters. He wondered whether it would not be wiser to ask old Mr. Thomas, the Senior African clerk, to entertain Hughes. At last he made a decision—he knew what he would do. He would ask Hughes to dinner at his bungalow and he would ask Hounslow, the agent of a large firm, to make up a third. Hounslow was English but born in East Africa, son of a Kenya settler. He would show by that that he had no prejudice. With the problem solved he turned to work with a lighter heart but with a mild sense of dissatisfaction.

Hughes arrived promptly after lunch. He was a tall man, probably in his early thirties, with a small military moustache, close-cropped hair, very dark skin, and even, white teeth, but he was completely unsmiling, and very polite. He shook hands with Sanderson, accepted a seat, refused a cigarette, and got down to business almost immediately. He listened to Sanderson carefully, made notes, and asked one or two questions. Sanderson called to Momoh to bring in the files. The clerk brought them in, put them down, and was going away when Sanderson stopped him suddenly, remembering his smile of pride, and introduced him to Hughes, who smiled pleasantly and briefly, shook hands and turned back to the files. Sanderson found this politeness and efficiency uncomfortable at first, and tried to soften the atmosphere with a joke here and there. But Hughes either did not understand or pretended he did not understand. At the end of a couple of hours most of the work was finished, and Sanderson asked Hughes what he would be doing that night. Then, feeling that the African engineer might regard it as an unwarrantable intrusion into his privacy, he added hastily, 'because I'd like you to come to dinner with me.'

'Yes, thank you, that will be nice,' Hughes answered, putting away his notes and getting up. Sanderson was a little disappointed that he had not shown more enthusiasm. Hang it all, he thought, I don't suppose many Europeans would ask him as I have done, but perhaps he is political and is accepting out of a sense of duty. Besides, he probably guesses why I asked him to come to the bungalow. 'You are sure you can manage it, by the way,' he said aloud.

'Oh, yes, thank you, that will be very nice,' Hughes repeated. 'I'll go and see the other official buildings now, and will be with you this evening. Good-bye, then, for the present,' he added. Sanderson walked with him to the door and they shook hands again while Momoh looked on admiringly.

Hounslow appeared at eight at Sanderson's bungalow and mixed himself a drink. He shouted through the door to Sanderson who was changing in his bedroom.

'Is anyone else coming to-night?'

'Hughes, the new assistant engineer,' Sanderson shouted back.

'What's he like? Does he come from Swansea, look you man?'

'No, he is an African—Mr. Oluyemi Egbert Hughes.'

There was a pause.

'Are you there, Hounslow?' Sanderson asked anxiously after a while.

'Yes, I am,' Hounslow replied through the door. 'Why didn't you tell me this before?'

'Because, frankly, I wasn't sure whether you'd come.'

'Are you afraid, Sanderson, of facing an educated black alone?'

'No, not at all, but I thought it would be good experience for you, my lad. It will correct some of your slave-driving ideas.'

'I am afraid he and I won't find much to say to each other,' Hounslow replied. 'Pity the club's closed to-night or I would have escaped before he arrived.'

Sanderson opened the door and entered the lounge-cum-dining-room. 'The club's closed?'

'Yes,' Hounslow said, 'a peculiar situation has arisen. We've run out of drinks through bad management,' he added.

'Why, were you going to take your Mr. Hughes there?'

'The idea had occurred to me,' Sanderson said, feeling relieved and somewhat guilty.

'There's no end to what you wallahs in the Administration will do to show your damned official broad-mindedness.'

He lit a cigarette and sank moodily into a chair. 'I wish I had brought my black missus with me,' he added, smiling reminiscently. 'She's a fine girl, you know,' he continued enthusiastically. 'Don't know what I'd do without her.'

'No, you certainly aren't bringing her : Mr. Hughes looks very respectable. And you're going to behave nicely to him, too.'

'Yes, teacher. Is he political?'

'I shouldn't wonder,' Sanderson answered. 'They all are, these chaps,you know, although they've got to conceal it when they're in the Service.'

'Shouldn't be surprised if he supplies copy to nationalist news-papers. However, we must move with the times,' Hounslow said resignedly. 'He'll probably get drunk and start smashing bottles,' he added hopefully.

In fact, they were all a little unsober before the evening was out. Olu Hughes appeared looking very smart in a light tropical suit and a black bow-tie.

'Oh, I forgot to tell you not to dress,' said Sanderson.

'Oh, that's all right,' Hughes replied.

Hounslow and Hughes were introduced to each other. The African said,'How do you do.'

Hounslow nodded. Neither shook hands. Sanderson mixed them drinks and made conversation about his garden.

They moved over to the other side of the room and sat down to chop. Sanderson waited for Hughes to begin before he himself started. Hughes waited for Sanderson because the latter was more senior in the Service, and in any case the array of knives and forks was a little confusing. Hounslow began as soon as the *hors d'œuvres* were placed in front of him. Then Sanderson put his knife and fork on his plate and passed Hughes the salt. Hughes took it and began to eat. Hounslow concentrated on the food and ate gloomily and slowly, now and again addressing a remark to Sanderson. Hughes, perhaps noticing this, turned slightly to Sanderson and spoke to him exclusively of his afternoon's work. Towards the end of the meal Hounslow, talking about rising prices, turned to Hughes and said, 'How are your people managing, Mr. Hughes, with all these rising prices? I suppose they're finding European food and clothes not quite so easy to maintain as they thought, eh?'

Hughes chewed his food silently for a few minutes. The silence became unbearable. Hounslow, beginning to frown, thinking he had been snubbed, was going to repeat his question in a louder voice. Sanderson, thinking the African was annoyed, was preparing to say something tactful. Hughes sipped some water, then, turning to Hounslow, said, 'Yes, they are finding European food and clothes hard to maintain.' Then he continued eating. Hounslow was not sure whether sarcasm was meant, and searched the African's face unsuccessfully for a sign. Sanderson said something about the rise in the cost of living hitting all classes, high and low, except the very rich, of course. 'Among which I dare say none of us is numbered. Let's go in and sit in more comfortable chairs and have coffee.'

Hounslow decided to relax, for he did not want to be boorish. Moreover, he was curious to know what Africans really thought; for he had never had the opportunity of talking to an African in such an atmosphere of equality. He addressed questions now and again to Hughes about what Africans thought on this or that matter, until the latter replied quietly that he was afraid he had been so busy lately that he had rather lost touch with the opinions of his people. Hounslow glanced sharply again to see whether any offence had been meant. Trouble is, he said to himself, you can never tell when these educated natives mean to be insolent or not. They all wear this damned mask of politeness; have not the courage of their convictions. But as the evening wore on and another bottle of whisky was opened, the atmosphere became more convivial. Sanderson turned to Hughes suddenly and said, 'You trained at home, didn't you? I mean in Britain. Where were you? London?'

'Yes, I was in London for most of the time, at one of the big Polytechnics near Oxford Circus. I lived in digs at Cricklewood and came up to the College every morning by bus.'

'Did you have good digs?' Sanderson asked.

Old Varsity men swapping reminiscences, Hounslow thought, a little contemptuously, stretching himself out on the chair easily. He will soon ask him, 'What was your first fifteen like?' and the darkie will say, 'Actually the forwards were not bad, a bit slow at passing perhaps, but not bad at all; we once drew with Rosslyn Park.' He helped himself sternly to some more whisky.

'I found a room eventually,' Hughes answered, 'after having several doors slammed in my face. It was quite a comfortable room and the landlady was a blonde, decent soul.'

Sanderson smiled. 'What a turn of phrase you have,' he said. 'But seriously, apart from the lodgings problem, did you enjoy your time in England?'

173

'Well, I didn't at first,' admitted Hughes, 'but later on I wasn't sure. It's the uncertainty of one's reception in England that confuses a lot of us. Sometimes you are welcomed with open arms by nice people. But on the other hand you get sudden rebuffs. Or what is worse, people simply avoid you as if you had some infectious disease. They are just cold and distant.'

Sanderson filled his glass slowly. 'I know what you mean,' he said, sipping his glass and then holding it up to the light. 'I worked in London, too, for a few months, and I found people very cold and distant. I often wondered whether there was something wrong with me. People behave very strangely in cities, you know, Hughes. They tend to be secretive and shy as a protection against the vastness surrounding them. And anything stranger than usual, like a man with a dark complexion, makes it even more so.'

Hounslow chuckled. 'By Jove, you are quite the Oxford man, Sanderson,' he said. 'You'll theorize your way to heaven and find it hellish when you get there.' He laughed at his own words, and then his brow swiftly darkened with heavy anger. 'You've got nothing to complain about,' he said to Hughes. 'Nor you either,' turning to Sanderson. 'I was the disappointed one in England. I grew up in Kenya and we thought of England as home all the time, and our old man told us all sorts of stories of the English countryside and our heritage. But when I went there to school nobody seemed to bother about the things we held dear.' He stretched himself on the chair. 'I don't suppose it was a good school,' he continued, 'but it was a public school all right. Headmasters' Conference and all that. It was well boosted in all the colonies, and there were special cheap rates for the holidays for boys whose parents were overseas. My father was a self-made man and left school early, and when he heard about this school he thought he would make up to us educationally for what he himself had missed.'

'Did you go back to East Africa when you left school?' Sanderson asked.

'No, I stayed on a little longer. But things were never quite the same. I worked for a time with a big exporting firm, but didn't like it particularly. Some of the chaps there thought I was a bit of a Blimp. They thought I was too narrow. People seemed to have changed so since my father's generation, whose ideas were what we colonials had. I mean white colonials, of course,' he added hastily.

'And how did you find it changed from what you had expected?' Hughes asked conversationally.

'Oh, in all sorts of ways,' Hounslow answered after a short pause, during which he had debated whether to admit Hughes freely into the conversation and had decided that for free and easy social

174

purposes the African could be an honorary white man for an evening. 'In all sorts of ways,' he repeated reflectively, nodding his head. 'Do you know,' he said, tapping Sanderson's knee, 'that one evening a chap tried to elbow me out of the way at the end of a show, during the National Anthem? I was standing at the end of a row, and the fellow gave me lip. Said I was to move on as he had a bus to catch, and not to block the gangway. Of course I refused to move and stood at attention. The chap leaned over and said into my ear, "Company at ease!" in a terribly common accent. I stood unflinching and he and his gang climbed over the seats and clattered out. Must have been Communists, of course. At the end of the "King" I rushed down the foyer looking for him to knock him down. But by then they had gone. Things like that made me sad,' he said, leaning back. 'No, the old country is not the same. Too much talk of freedom, equality and democracy, and not enough doing things.'

'I don't think they are as bad as that,' put in Sanderson, feeling things were rather up to him. 'You'll find things have changed in the larger cities, but curiously enough, London itself and the country-side remain always unchanged. What did you really think of London?' he said, turning to Hughes.

'Ah, London was full of wonders for me. It was the organization of everything and the clockwork efficiency which amazed me. You English are efficient. I used to go for walks at night and watch the traffic lights changing to yellow, to red, to green, to yellow again all through the night. When I was studying hard for exams I would go out at two to three in the morning to clear my brain before going to bed. Once I saw a huge motor lorry stop at a crossroad early when the lights were against it. There was no one about, not even a policeman in sight, and I was in the shadow. But he stopped just because the lights were against him. That's what I call organization and a sense of the right thing. I never shall forget that moment. Further—that moment summarized London and the English for me.' There was a pause for a few moments, and the other two looked obviously impressed. Hughes shut his eyes slightly and thought again of the Cricklewood Broadway he had so often loved but hated sometimes with a weary homesickness in the grey winter. 'To London,' he said, suddenly raising his glass.

'To London,' the others murmured. 'God bless her!'

'But mind you, I was glad to be back home,' Hughes added after a while, fearing they might think him a 'black Englishman,' which he most dreaded. 'There are things a man can do in this country which he cannot do in England.'

'For example?' Hounslow asked, with some interest.

'Well, you can start things single-handed, and finish them before your own eyes here, while you'd have to be a genius to do that in England.'

'I don't know about beginning and finishing things here,' Sanderson began.

'I've built a bridge here,' Hughes interrupted. 'I came by this district last year, about four miles from here, on the Yolahun road, and there was a dry stream-bed which people used as a short cut to the big market in the dry season, but in the rains the stream was too swift for them to ford and it took them about two hours to make a detour to cross it farther up on a swinging rope bridge. In fact, that's why for generations you'd have a small famine in this district during the rains, because most people simply did not bother or could not travel properly to the large town to sell their crops and buy food. I simply couldn't understand why nobody had thought of building a bridge there before.

'Perhaps they thought of it during the rains, but forgot about it in the dry season. That often happens in this country. Or, again, people may simply have accepted it.'

'So *you* built that bridge! I wondered about it,' Sanderson said. 'I thought it was the army, but it looked too permanent for them.'

'I expect it's improved things quite a lot now, hasn't it?' Hughes asked with some triumph.

Sanderson wondered whether it was kinder to leave the truth unsaid, because in fact the bridge was seldom used by the villagers and then only by motor transport. Someone had been drowned years ago at that point, and the local legend had it there was a water-spirit there during the rains.

'Yes, I think it has improved things,' he said aloud.

'That's much sooner than I expected,' Hughes said. 'Do you know some years ago someone was drowned there? And people think there is a devil round there during the rains. In fact, I had to hire a more powerful medicine-man to sacrifice a chicken on the site and pour some rum on the ground before the labourers would begin.'

'As you know,' said Hounslow with jovial politeness, 'we prefer champagne. Break a bottle of the stuff over the prow of a ship as she slides off her slipway, just to appease the old gods. Same as you, old man; same as you.'

'Of course, I had the chicken and the rest of the rum for dinner that evening,' Hughes said, trying to show that he had treated the whole thing as a piece of whimsy to humour his workmen and had never for a moment taken it seriously. At the same time he thought Hounslow had been patronizingly polite, trying to compare it with an English custom. He had himself seen a new ship being launched at a shipyard, and had been awed by it. Of course, the ceremony bore no comparison with the blood of a white chicken and the rum poured out by a simple misguided native. In fact, in the launching on Clydeside there had even been a milord about. He had had him pointed out. It bore no comparison. Anyhow, he thought, perhaps I am too sensitive.

'I envy you chaps—engineers, doctors, agriculturalists and so on,' Sanderson said. 'You begin things, you finish them, and you see the result. But we never do. We never even know if we've begun. Nor when we finish. We never really know whether we are just redundant.'

Hughes was touched. 'Oh, no no,' he cried, 'you administrators, white or black, will always be needed to plan things and to manage men. When we are old and finished, then there is an end to us as engineers. Then we begin to learn your job, to administer. But I must go,' he said springing up, 'I've got to set off early to-morrow, and I know you will forgive me.' He shook hands with both, and swiftly disappeared in spite of Sanderson's protesting that he could put him up for the night. And Hounslow pressed the other man's whisky on him, to take just one more for the road.

After the African had left, Hounslow strolled up and down the room, stumbling a little. Then he stopped suddenly in front of Sanderson, who was slowly puffing a pipe. 'Do you know,' he said, in a voice of such tiredness that the other glanced up swiftly—'do you know that apropos of what you said a few minutes ago, I am beginning to feel particularly redundant in this damned country!' He sat down and rested his head on the edge of the table, with his body sprawling loosely in the chair.

'But you are not an Administrator,' Sanderson said, 'you are the senior agent of a very prosperous firm.'

'No, I'm feeling *de trop* in a different sort of way, especially when I meet educated natives like our mutual friend here this evening. They brought us up as children saying that Africa was a white man's country, and that for centuries to come we were to help and teach the black man slowly and certainly what it had taken us hundreds of years to gain. But here in my own lifetime I see these people trained to do all sorts of things, and the trouble is they sometimes do them well. Mind you, I don't say they are as good as we are. They can never be that.'

'Yes,' said Sanderson swiftly, 'just as we couldn't be them if we tried. We and they are both different, but good in our separate ways.'

'Yes, yes, I suppose you've got to say that in your position,'

Hounslow replied. 'But whatever you say, I don't think they can do it in a generation, old man; they'll crack up when things go bad. That chap Hughes, for example, was frightened of the water-juju: I could see it in his face.' He filled his glass himself and emptied it. 'All the same, old man, they make us feel useless—damned useless. You Whitehall chaps can't see that you are trying to put us, your own kith and kin, out into the cold. You'd be surprised how hard I found it to get this job. And now Headquarters is talking about training African assistant managers. As if I didn't know what they meant! Why are you always trying to be fair, you Johnnies? Always pushing us out into the cold?' He burst into tears. Sanderson tried first not to notice; then gave it up, went over and stood by him, putting his hand on Hounslow's shoulder. 'Don't you think the country is big enough for Hughes and you and me? Hughes has to be here because it's his country. You are here because no man can do everything in his own country. I think this idea of a man's country belonging to him is a phase we all pass through. *We* passed through it fifty years ago. Only his country-side and the profitless patches in his country belong to any man. The fat of the land is to whoever can get it, and whoever that is then tries to belong to the country even more than those whose heritage it was. It is by this eternal recruitment of the fittest alien that great nations and privileged classes survive. And that is why you'll always be here if you are good enough, Hounslow, and for no other reason.'

The other man had been listening with attention. 'I wish I'd been educated your way, Sanderson. I wish I knew what words meant and could use them. But I gather it's a case of the survival of the fittest.' The wind rose and fell, rattling the windows.

'So you think there will be room for all of us?' he said, getting up and stretching. 'I doubt it; you only have to read the local rag. But it is not a bad country, all said and done. A man can see results in it sometimes.'

'To Africa,' Sanderson toasted gravely.

'Yes, yes, to Africa; white man's country and black man's, too.' Hounslow nodded, sipping. 'A last one before I go, one for the road, so to speak,' he added, nodding all the time as if comforted but only half convinced. Sanderson picked up the bottle. But it was empty.

'Never mind,' Hounslow said thickly, 'we'll have it in soda.' He was feeling tired, sad, and then happy.

Sanderson filled the glasses. And the little pearly bubbles clung to the sides of the glasses to burst to the surface. They tickled Hounslow's nostrils, and he grimaced happily.

'Whom shall it be to this time?' Sanderson asked.

'To you, to you, old man,' Hounslow said affectionately. 'To you, old man, and me,' he chuckled.

'And Olu Hughes too?' Sanderson added.

'Yes, him too,' Hounslow agreed. 'In fact, to all good chaps everywhere. "For we are jolly good fellows,"' he hummed as he searched for his car key.

Sanderson saw him off from the small courtyard in front of his bungalow. 'Are you sure you will be able to drive yourself home?' he asked him.

'Positive, old man, I can drive home blindfolded. Give us a shove, there's a good fellow.'

Sanderson heaved and pushed for a while before the car broke into life and careered off. It headed in the opposite direction from the town, and Sanderson shouted to Hounslow to stop and turn round. But the car was soon lost to sight, although the sound could be heard in the distance. Sanderson went indoors with misgiving and wearily prepared for bed.

Hounslow put the car into gear and roared up a hill. The throb of the engine filled him with an exultant power, as did an occasional gust of wind. He knew where he was going and he felt his head strangely clear. After about fifteen minutes he slowed down and stopped. He bent over his wheel and listened to the shrill call of the cicadas and the deep bass croaking of the frogs; these would stop suddenly sometimes and an eerie silence filled the heavy air. He left the head-lamps on and walked forward slowly in the broad beam of light to examine the bridge more closely. It was an ordinary one but strong, concrete and with a simple, hard grace. He stood in the middle of it and jumped up and down, as if half hoping it would break. He leaned over one side and watched the growing waters between the rocks. He threw a twig in on one side and rushed over to the other side to see it appear, laughing with pleasure when it did so. Then he walked slowly back to his car. And Olu Hughes, standing by the shadows, where he had hidden when he had first heard the car, marvelled that Hounslow had not detected his presence, his heart had been beating so loudly. He had walked far out of town to come and see the bridge he had fashioned with love and care. He had come in the dark of night, defying the dark to show himself that he was not afraid of the water-spirit. He had been strangely pleased and a little puzzled at the look on the white man's face as he strode past slowly.

It leaped suddenly into the middle of the road and stood there, poised, dazzled by the light from the head-lamps. Hounslow sat quickly upright in the driver's seat to watch it. Hughes restrained a startled cry and gazed with fascination. It was a curious beast. It had the shape of an antelope but was reddish-brown on the back and white underneath, with a sharp boundary-line between the two colours as if it had been swimming and washed off its colour. It had slender curved horns on a head held proudly and supported on a delicate neck. It had black vertical stripes down each buttock and one on its back continuing to the tail. It stood there for a few long seconds. Hounslow then sounded his horn sharply and the beast bounded high into the air and forward, to be lost as suddenly as it had appeared, like a secret memory.

'Oh, it's only a red-buck,' Hounslow shouted aloud, as he thought, to himself. He started the car, reversed carefully into the side of the road, and turned round and drove back steadily to town.

It was, after all, only a red-buck, an impala, that they were afraid of, Hughes meditated as he climbed on to the bridge. He put the small spirit-level he always carried about with him on one of the railings and shone his torch on it. He nodded with satisfaction as he watched the air-bubble oscillate and settle in the centre; and then, reluctantly, he started to walk back to the rest-house. He stopped suddenly, held out his hand a moment or so, and then broke into a steady run. For the rain had begun to fall in single heavy drops like the slow, quiet weeping of a woman proud, proud to distraction for an only son, yet vaguely afraid.

Ghana[1]

KWAME NKRUMAH

AMONG the colonial peoples, there is a vast, untapped reservoir of peace and goodwill towards Britain, would she but divest herself of the outmoded, moth-eaten trappings of two centuries ago, and present herself to her colonial peoples in a new and shining vestment and hand us the olive branch of peace and love, and give us a guiding hand in working out our own destinies.

In the very early days of the Christian era, long before England had assumed any importance, long even before her people had

[1] Extract from Dr. Nkrumah's speech of July 1953, known as 'The Motion of Destiny,' when he formally proposed the independence of the Gold Coast.

united into a nation, our ancestors had attained a great empire, which lasted until the eleventh century, when it fell before the attacks of the Moors of the North. At its height that empire stretched from Timbuktu to Bamako, and even as far as to the Atlantic. It is said that lawyers and scholars were much respected in that empire and that the inhabitants of Ghana wore garments of wool, cotton, silk and velvet. There was trade in copper, gold and textile fabrics, and jewels and weapons of gold and silver were carried.

Thus may we take pride in the name of Ghana, not out of romanticism, but as an inspiration for the future. It is right and proper that we should know about our past. For just as the future moves from the present so the present has emerged from the past. Nor need we be ashamed of our past. There was much in it of glory. What our ancestors achieved in the context of their contemporary society gives us confidence that we can create, out of that past, a glorious future, not in terms of war and military pomp, but in terms of social progress and of peace. For we repudiate war and violence. Our battles shall be against the old ideas that keep men trammelled in their own greed ; against the crass stupidities that breed hatred, fear and inhumanity. The heroes of our future will be those who can lead our people out of the stifling fog of disintegration through serfdom, into the valley of light where purpose, endeavour and determination will create that brotherhood which Christ proclaimed two thousand years ago, and about which so much is said, but so little done.

Epilogue

Tell Freedom

PETER ABRAHAMS

🌺

'And judgement is turned away backward, and justice standeth afar off:
for truth is fallen in the street, and equity cannot enter.' ISAIAH.

WEDNESDAY was crackling day. On that day the children of
the location made the long trek to Elsburg siding for the squares
of pig's rind that passed for our daily meat. We collected a double
lot of cow dung the day before; a double lot of *moeroga*.[1]

I finished my breakfast and washed up. Aunt Liza was at her
wash-tub in the yard. A misty, sickly sun was just showing. And on
the open veld the frost lay thick and white on the grass.

'Ready?' Aunt Liza called.

I went out to her. She shook the soapsuds off her swollen hands
and wiped them on her apron. She lifted the apron and put her
hand through the slits of the many thin cotton dresses she wore.
The dress nearest the skin was the one with the pocket. From this
she pulled a sixpenny piece. She tied it in a knot in the corner of
a bit of coloured cloth.

'Take care of that. . . . Take the smaller piece of bread in the
bin but don't eat it till you start back. You can have a small piece
of crackling with it. Only a small piece, understand?'

'Yes, Aunt Liza.'

'All right.'

I got the bread and tucked it into the little canvas bag in which
I would carry the crackling.

'Bye, Aunt Liza.' I trotted off, one hand in my pocket, feeling the
cloth where the money was. I paused at Andries's home.

'Andries!' I danced up and down while I waited. The cold was
not so terrible on bare feet if one did not keep still.

Andries came trotting out of their yard. His mother's voice
followed; desperate and plaintive:

'I'll skin you if you lose the money!'

'Women!' Andries said bitterly.

[1] Wild spinach.

I glimpsed the dark, skinny woman at her wash-tub as we trotted across the veld. Behind, and in front of us, other children trotted in twos and threes.

There was a sharp bite to the morning air I sucked in; it stung my nose so that tears came to my eyes; it went down my throat like an icy draught; my nose ran. I tried breathing through my mouth but this was worse. The cold went through my shirt and shorts; my skin went pimply and chilled; my fingers went numb and began to ache; my feet felt like frozen lumps that did not belong to me, yet jarred and hurt each time I put them down. I began to feel sick and desperate.

'Jesus God in heaven!' Andries cried suddenly.

I looked at him. His eyes were rimmed in red. Tears ran down his cheeks. His face was drawn and purple, a sick look on it.

'Faster,' I said.

'Think it'll help?'

I nodded. We went faster. We passed two children, sobbing and moaning as they ran. We were all in the same desperate situation. We were creatures haunted and hounded by the cold. It was a cruel enemy who gave no quarter. And our means of fighting it were pitifully inadequate. In all the mornings and evenings of the winter months, young and old, big and small, were helpless victims of the bitter cold. Only towards noon and the early afternoon, when the sun sat high in the sky, was there a brief respite. For us, the children, the cold, especially the morning cold, assumed an awful and malevolent personality. We talk of 'It.' 'It' was a half-human monster with evil thoughts, evil intentions, bent on destroying us. 'It' was happiest when we were most miserable. Andries had told me how 'It' had, last winter, caught and killed a boy.

Hunger was an enemy too, but one with whom we could come to terms, who had many virtues and values. Hunger gave our *pap*,[1] *moeroga,* and crackling a feast-like quality. We could, when it was not with us, think and talk kindly about it. Its memory could even give moments of laughter. But the cold of winter was with us all the time. 'It' never really eased up. There were only more bearable degrees of 'It' at high noon and on mild days. 'It' was the real enemy. And on this Wednesday morning, as we ran across the veld, winter was more bitterly, bitingly, freezingly, real than ever.

The sun climbed. The frozen earth thawed, leaving the short grass looking wet and weary. Painfully, our feet and legs came alive. The aching numbness slowly left our fingers. We ran more slowly in the more bearable cold.

In climbing, the sun lost some of its damp look and seemed a

[1] A kind of porridge made with crushed maize.

real, if cold, sun. When it was right overhead, we struck the sandy road which meant we were nearing the siding. None of the others were in sight. Andries and I were alone on the sandy road on the open veld. We slowed down to a brisk walk. We were sufficiently thawed to want to talk.

'How far?' I said.

'A few minutes,' he said.

'I've got a piece of bread,' I said.

'Me too,' he said. 'Let's eat it now.'

'On the way back,' I said. 'With a bit of crackling.'

'Good idea. . . . Race to the fork.'

'All right.'

'Go!' he said.

We shot off together, legs working like pistons. He soon pulled away from me. He reached the fork in the road some fifty yards ahead.

'I win!' he shouted gleefully, though his teeth still chattered.

We pitched stones down the road, each trying to pitch further than the other. I won and wanted to go on doing it. But Andries soon grew weary with pitching. We raced again. Again he won. He wanted another race but I refused. I wanted pitching, but he refused. So, sulking with each other, we reached the pig farm.

We followed a fenced-off pathway round sprawling white buildings. Everywhere about us was the grunt of pigs. As we passed an open doorway, a huge dog came bounding out, snarling and barking at us. In our terror, we forgot it was fenced in and streaked away. Surprised, I found myself a good distance ahead of Andries. We looked back and saw a young white woman call the dog to heel.

'Damn Boer dog,' Andries said.

'Matter with it?' I asked.

'They teach them to go for us. Never get caught by one. My old man's got a hole in his bottom where a Boer dog got him.'

I remembered I had outstripped him.

'I won!' I said.

'Only because you were frightened,' he said.

'I still won.'

'Scare arse,' he jeered.

'Scare arse, yourself!'

'I'll knock you!'

'I'll knock you back!'

A couple of white men came down the path and ended our possible fight. We hurried past them to the distant shed where a queue had already formed. There were grown-ups and children. All the grown-ups, and some of the children, were from places other than our location.

The line moved slowly. The young white man who served us did it in leisurely fashion, with long pauses for a smoke. Occasionally he turned his back.

At last, after what seemed hours, my turn came. Andries was behind me. I took the sixpenny piece from the square of cloth and offered it to the man.

'Well?' he said.

'Sixpence crackling, please.'

Andries nudged me in the back. The man's stare suddenly became cold and hard. Andries whispered into my ear.

'Well?' the man repeated coldly.

'Please, *baas*,'[1] I said.

'What d'you want?'

'Sixpence crackling, please.'

'What?'

Andries dug me in the ribs.

'Sixpence crackling, please, *baas*.'

'What?'

'Sixpence crackling, please, *baas*.'

'You new here?'

'Yes, *baas*.' I looked at his feet while he stared at me.

At last he took the sixpenny piece from me. I held my bag open while he filled it with crackling from a huge pile on a large canvas sheet on the ground. Turning away, I stole a fleeting glance at his face. His eyes met mine, and there was amused, challenging mockery in them. I waited for Andries at the back of the queue, out of the reach of the white man's mocking eyes.

The cold day was at its mildest as we walked home along the sandy road. I took out my piece of bread and, with a small piece of greasy crackling, still warm, on it, I munched as we went along. We had not yet made our peace so Andries munched his bread and crackling on the other side of the road.

'Dumb fool!' he mocked at me for not knowing how to address the white man.

'Scare arse!' I shouted back.

Thus, hurling curses at each other, we reached the fork. Andries saw them first and moved over to my side of the road.

'White boys,' he said.

There were three of them. Two of about our own size and one slightly bigger. They had school bags and were coming toward us up the road from the siding.

[1] Master.

187

'Better run for it,' Andries said.

'Why?'

'No, that'll draw them. Let's just walk along, but quickly.'

'Why?' I repeated.

'Shut up,' he said.

Some of his anxiety touched me. Our own scrap was forgotten. We marched side by side as fast as we could. The white boys saw us and hurried up the road. We passed the fork. Perhaps they would take the turning away from us. We dared not look back.

'Hear them?' Andries asked.

'No.'

I looked over my shoulder.

'They're coming,' I said.

'Walk faster,' Andries said. 'If they come closer, run.'

'Hey, *Klipkop!*' [1]

'Don't look back,' Andries said.

'Hottentot!'

We walked as fast as we could.

'Bloody kaffir!'

Ahead was a bend in the road. Behind the bend were bushes. Once there, we could run without them knowing it till it was too late.

'Faster,' Andries said.

They began pelting us with stones.

'Run when we get to the bushes,' Andries said.

The bend and the bushes were near. We would soon be there.

A clear young voice carried to us:

'Your fathers are dirty black bastards of baboons!'

'Run!' Andries called.

A violent, unreasoning anger suddenly possessed me. I stopped and turned.

'You're a liar!' I screamed it.

The foremost boy pointed at me:

'An ugly black baboon!'

In a fog of rage I went towards him.

'Liar!' I shouted. 'My father was better than your father!'

I neared them. The bigger boy stepped between me and the one I was after.

'My father was better than your father! Liar!'

The big boy struck me a mighty clout on the side of the face. I staggered, righted myself, and leapt at the boy who had insulted my father. I struck him on the face, hard. A heavy blow on the

___
[1] Lit. Stonehead.

back of my head nearly stunned me. I grabbed at the boy in front of me. We went down together.

'Liar!' I said through clenched teeth, hitting him with all my might.

Blows rained on me, on my head, my neck, the side of my face, my mouth, but my enemy was under me and I pounded him fiercely, all the time repeating:

'Liar! Liar! Liar!'

Suddenly, stars exploded in my head. Then there was darkness.

I emerged from the darkness to find Andries kneeling beside me.

'God, man! I thought they'd killed you.'

I sat up. The white boys were nowhere to be seen. Like Andries, they'd probably thought me dead and run off in panic. The inside of my mouth felt sore and swollen. My nose was tender to the touch. The back of my head ached. A trickle of blood dripped from my nose. I stemmed it with the square of coloured cloth. The greatest damage was to my shirt. It was ripped in many places. I remembered the crackling. I looked anxiously about. It was safe, a little off the road on the grass. I relaxed. I got up and brushed my clothes. I picked up the crackling.

'God, you're dumb!' Andries said. 'You're going to get it! Dumb arse!'

I was too depressed to retort. Besides, I knew he was right. I was dumb. I should have run when he told me to.

'Come on,' I said.

One of many small groups of children, each child carrying his little bag of crackling, we trod the long road home in the cold winter afternoon.

There was tension in the house that night. When I got back Aunt Liza had listened to the story in silence. The beating or scolding I expected did not come. But Aunt Liza changed while she listened, became remote and withdrawn. When Uncle Sam came home she told him what had happened. He, too, just looked at me and became more remote and withdrawn than usual. They were waiting for something; their tension reached out to me, and I waited with them, anxious, apprehensive.

The thing we waited for came while we were having our supper. We heard a trap pull up outside.

'Here it is,' Uncle Sam said and got up.

Aunt Liza leaned back from the table and put her hands in her lap, fingers intertwined, a cold, unseeing look in her eyes.

Before Uncle Sam reached it, the door burst open. A tall, broad, white man strode in. Behind him came the three boys. The one I had attacked had swollen lips and a puffy left eye.

'Evening, *baas!*' Uncle Sam murmured.

'That's him,' the bigger boy said, pointing at me.

The white man stared till I lowered my eyes.

'Well?' he said.

'He's sorry, *baas*,' Uncle Sam said quickly. 'I've given him a hiding he won't forget soon. You know how it is, *baas*. He's new here, the child of a relative in Johannesburg and they don't all know how to behave there. You know how it is in the big towns, *baas*.' The plea in Uncle Sam's voice had grown more pronounced as he went on. He turned to me. 'Tell the *baas* and young *basies* how sorry you are, Lee.'

I looked at Aunt Liza and something in her lifelessness made me stubborn in spite of my fear.

'He insulted my father,' I said.

The white man smiled.

'See, Sam, your hiding couldn't have been good.'

There was a flicker of life in Aunt Liza's eyes. For a brief moment she saw me, looked at me, warmly, lovingly, then her eyes went dead again.

'He's only a child, *baas*,' Uncle Sam murmured.

'You stubborn too, Sam?'

'No, *baas*.'

'Good. . . . Then teach him, Sam. If you and he are to live here, you must teach him. Well. . . . ?'

'Yes, *baas*.'

Uncle Sam went into the other room and returned with a thick leather thong. He wound it once round his hand and advanced on me. The man and boys leaned against the door, watching. I looked at Aunt Liza's face. Though there was no sign of life or feeling on it, I knew suddenly, instinctively, that she wanted me not to cry.

Bitterly, Uncle Sam said :

'You must never lift your hand to a white person. No matter what happens, you must never lift your hand to a white person . . .'

He lifted the strap and brought it down on my back. I clenched my teeth and stared at Aunt Liza. I did not cry with the first three strokes. Then, suddenly, Aunt Liza went limp. Tears showed in her eyes. The thong came down on my back, again and again. I screamed and begged for mercy. I grovelled at Uncle Sam's feet, begging him to stop, promising never to lift my hand to any white person. . . .

At last, the white man's voice said :

'All right, Sam.'

Uncle Sam stopped. I lay whimpering on the floor. Aunt Liza sat like one in a trance.

'Is he still stubborn, Sam?'

'Tell the *baas* and *basies* you are sorry.'

'I'm sorry,' I said.

'Bet his father is one of those who believe in equality.'

'His father is dead,' Aunt Liza said.

'Good night, Sam.'

'Good night, *baas*. Sorry about this.'

'All right, Sam.' He opened the door. The boys went out first, then he followed. 'Good night, Liza.'

Aunt Liza did not answer. The door shut behind the white folk, and soon we heard their trap moving away. Uncle Sam flung the thong viciously against the door, slumped down on the bench, folded his arms on the table, and buried his head on his arms. Aunt Liza moved away from him, came on the floor beside me and lifted me into her large lap. She sat rocking my body. Uncle Sam began to sob softly. After some time, he raised his head and looked at us.

'Explain to the child, Liza,' he said.

'You explain,' Aunt Liza said bitterly. 'You are the man. You did the beating. You are the head of the family. This is a man's world. You do the explaining.'

'Please, Liza . . . .'

'You should be happy. The whites are satisfied. We can go on now.'

With me in her arms, Aunt Liza got up. She carried me into the other room. The food on the table remained half eaten. She laid me on the bed on my stomach, smeared fat on my back, then covered me with the blankets. She undressed and got into bed beside me. She cuddled me close, warmed me with her own body. With her big hand on my cheek, she rocked me, first to silence, then to sleep.

For the only time of my stay there, I slept on a bed in Elsburg.

When I woke next morning Uncle Sam had gone. Aunt Liza only once referred to the beating he had given me. It was in the late afternoon, when I returned with the day's cow dung.

'It hurt him,' she said. 'You'll understand one day.'

That night, Uncle Sam brought me an orange, a bag of boiled sweets, and a dirty old picture book. He smiled as he gave them to me, rather anxiously. When I smiled back at him, he seemed to relax. He put his hand on my head, started to say something, then changed his mind and took his seat by the fire.

Aunt Liza looked up from the floor where she dished out the food.

'It's all right, old man,' she murmured.

'One day . . . . ' Uncle Sam said.

'It's all right,' Aunt Liza repeated insistently.

The long winter passed. Slowly, day by day, the world of Elsburg became a warmer place. The cracks in my feet began to heal. The spells of bearable, noonday cold gave way to warmth. The noise of the veld at night became a din. The freezing nights changed, became bearable; changed again, became warm. Warm nights and hot days!

Summer had come, and with its coming the world became a softer, kindlier, more beautiful place. Sunflowers began blooming in people's yards. And people themselves began to relax and laugh. When, one evening, as I came in with some washing from the line, I heard Uncle Sam's voice raised in laughter, and saw him and Aunt Liza playing, I knew the summer had really come. Later that same evening he went into the other room and returned with a guitar. Aunt Liza beamed.

'Open the door?'

Uncle Sam nodded. He played. Soon people from the other houses came, in ones and twos, till our little room was crowded. Someone sang with his arms on his wife's shoulders, a love song :

> *I'll be your sweetheart,*
> *If you will be mine . . . .*

Summer had come indeed.

In the long summer afternoons, after my day's work, I went down to the river. Sometimes Andries and some of the other children went with me. Often I went alone.

Often, with others, or alone, I climbed the short willows with their long drooping branches. The touch of willow leaf on the cheek gives a feeling of cool wonder. Often I jumped from stone to stone on the broad bed of the shallow, clear, fast-flowing river. Sometimes I found little pools of idle water, walled off by stones from the flow. I tickled long-tailed tadpoles in these. The sun on the water touched their bodies with myriad colours. Sometimes I watched the *springhaas*—the wild rabbit of the veld—go leaping across the land, almost faster than my eye could follow. And some-times I lay on my back, on the green grass; on the bank of the river, and looked up at the distant sky, watching thin fleecy white clouds form and re-form and trying to associate the shapes with people and things I knew. I loved being alone by the river. It became my special world.

Each day I explored a little more of the river, going further up or down stream, extending the frontiers of my world. One day, going further downstream than I had been before, I came upon a boy. He was on the bank on the other side from me. We saw each other at the same time and stared. He was completely naked. He carried two finely carved sticks of equal size and shape, both about his own height. He was not light brown, like the other children of our location, but dark brown, almost black. I moved almost to the edge of the river. He called out in a strange language.

'Hello!' I shouted.

He called out again, and again I could not understand. I searched for a place with stones, then bounded across. I approached him slowly. As I drew near, he gripped his sticks more firmly. I stopped.

He spoke harshly, flung one stick on the ground at my feet, and held the other ready as though to fight.

'Don't want to fight,' I said.

I reached down to pick up the stick and return it to him. He took a step forward and raised the one in his hand. I moved back quickly. He stepped back and pointed at the stick on the ground. I shook my head.

'Don't want to fight.'

I pushed the stick towards him with my foot, ready to run at the first sign of attack. I showed my new, stubby teeth in a tentative smile. He said something that sounded less aggressive. I nodded, smiling more broadly. He relaxed, picked up the stick, and transferred both to his left hand. He smacked his chest.

'Joseph! Zulu!'

I smacked my own chest.

'Lee . . . .' But I didn't know what I was apart from that.

He held out his hand. We shook. His face lit up in a sunny smile. He said something and pointed downstream. Then he took my arm and led me down.

Far downstream, where the river skirted a hillside, hidden by a cluster of willows, we came on a large clear pool. Joseph flung his sticks on the ground and dived in. He shot through the water like a tadpole. He went down and came up. He shouted and beckoned me to come in. I undressed and went in more tentatively. Laughing, he pulled me under. I came up gasping and spluttering, my belly filled with water. He smacked me on the back and the water shot out of my mouth in a rush. When he realized I could not swim he became more careful. We spent the afternoon with Joseph teaching me to swim. At home, that evening, I stood beside Aunt Liza's wash-tub.

'Aunt Liza . . . .'

'Yes?'

'What am I?'

'What are you talking about?'

'I met a boy at the river. He said he was Zulu.'

She laughed.

'You are Coloured. There are three kinds of people: white people, Coloured people and black people. The white people come first, then the Coloured people, then the black people.'

'Why?'

'Because it is so.'

Next day, when I met Joseph, I smacked my chest and said: 'Lee Coloured!'

He clapped his hands and laughed.

Joseph and I spent most of the long summer afternoons together. He learnt some Afrikaans from me; I learnt some Zulu from him. Our days were full.

There was the river to explore.

There were my swimming lessons, and others.

I learnt to fight with sticks; to weave a green hat of young willow wands and leaves; to catch frogs and tadpoles with my hands; to set a trap for the *springhaas;* to make the sounds of the river birds.

There was the hot sun to comfort us . . . .

There was the green grass to dry our bodies . . . .

There was the soft clay with which to build . . . .

There was the fine sand with which to fight . . . .

There were our giant grasshoppers to race . . . .

There were the locust swarms when the skies turned black and we caught them by the hundreds . . . .

There was the rare taste of crisp, brown baked, salted locusts . . . .

There was the voice of the wind in the willows . . . .

There was the voice of the heaven in the thunderstorms . . . .

There were the voices of two children in laughter, ours . . . .

There were Joseph's tales of black kings who lived in days before the white man . . . .

At home, I said:

'Aunt Liza . . . .'

'Yes?'

'Did we have Coloured kings before the white man?'

'No.'

'Then where did we come from? Joseph and his mother come from the black kings who were before the white man.'

And laughing, and ruffling my head, she said:

'You talk too much. . . . Go'n wash up.'

And to Joseph, next day, I said :
'We didn't have Coloured kings before the white man.'
And he comforted me and said :
'It is of no moment. You are my brother. Now my kings will be your kings. Come : I have promised the mother to bring you home. She awaits you. I will race you to the hill.'
From the top of the hill I looked into a long valley where cattle grazed. To the right, on the sloping land, nestled a cluster of mud huts. Round each hut was a wall built of mud.
'That is my home.' Joseph pointed.
We veered right and went down to it. From a distance, we saw a woman at the gate of one of the huts.
'There is the mother !' He walked faster.
She was barefooted. She wore a slight skirt that came above her knees. A child was strapped to her back. The upper part of her body was naked except for the cloth across her chest that supported the child. Round her neck, arms, and legs were strings of white beads. As we drew near, I saw that she was young. And her broad, round face was beautiful. Her black eyes were liquid soft. She called out a greeting and smiled. Joseph pushed me forward.
'This is my brother, Lee of the Coloureds, little mother.'
'Greetings, Mother,' I said.
'I greet you, my son,' she said softly, a twinkle in her eyes.
'As the man of my house has told you, food awaits. Come.'
'See !' Joseph puffed out his chest. To his mother he said, 'He would not believe when I told him I was the man in our house.'
'He is indeed,' she said.
Circling the hut was a raised platform. We sat on this while she brought us the food ; salted fried locusts and corn on the cob. She sat nearby and watched us eating.
'Show the mother,' Joseph said, and took another bite at the *mielies*. 'Show the mother you are not circumcised yet.'
I showed her.
'This is strange,' she said. 'Have you no initiation schools?'
'No !' Joseph said.
'Then when do you enter manhood?'
'He does not know.'
'Is it true?' She looked at me.
I nodded.
'He's still a child !' Joseph cried. 'So big and a child !'

Christmas came and it was a feast of eating and laughter. I spent half my time at home with Aunt Liza and Uncle Sam and the other half with Joseph and the little mother.

My sixth birthday came. Joseph and the little mother and I celebrated it by the river.

Then, early one morning, just as the first cold touches crept into the morning air, Joseph came to our location.

I was washing up when I heard young voices shouting :

'Look at the naked kaffir ! Lee's kaffir !'

I rushed out. Joseph came gravely to me.

'I come to take leave, my brother. My father has died in the mines so we go back to our land.'

He stood straight and stern, not heeding the shouts of the children about. He was a man. This was the burden of his manhood. I had learned much from him, so I said equally coldly :

'I must take leave of the little mother.'

'She is a woman. She weeps.'

We ran all the way there . . . .

When the little cart had taken them away, I climbed the hill and went down to the river. I carried Joseph's two sticks with me. These were his parting gift to his brother.

'Defend yourself,' he had said. 'I will make others.'

I walked along the river that had been our kingdom. Now it was a desolate place. Joseph had been here with me ; now Joseph had gone. Before I realized it, my tears flowed fast. There had been much between us.

So the summer passed. The autumn came. The leaves went brown on the willows by the river. They fluttered to the ground and turned to mould. The long days shortened suddenly. The cold came. Winter had come to torture us again.

About the Authors

✿

S. F. ABODERIN was born some thirty-two years ago in West Africa, where he was educated. Later he studied social science in England, afterwards returning to Nigeria where he has been working in the Social Welfare Department in Ibadan.

PETER ABRAHAMS was born in 1919 at Vrededorp, one of the slums of Johannesburg. His father was an Ethiopian and his mother a Cape Coloured. His father died when he was five years old and it was then that he went to live with his aunt and uncle in Elsburg, a village in the Transvaal. The extract given here from his book, *Tell Freedom*, gives a picture of some of the incidents of his life there. When he was nine, he went to work for a tinsmith for a wage of 2/6 a week. Whilst he was working there, a young Jewish typist in the office told him stories from *Lamb's Tales from Shakespeare*, which fired his imagination and determined him to endeavour to attend school in order to learn to read and write.

During the years that followed, he managed to go to school spasmodically. In between whiles, he worked as a slops-boy in an hotel, an office boy, and a carrier in the market, among other things.

In 1935 he left school and wandered about South Africa. With a friend, he started a school for the poor people of the Cape Flats near Cape Town. In 1939 he was among the unemployed of Durban. There he signed on a ship as a stoker and after two years at sea he worked his way to England. He settled in England and became well known as an author. He left England in 1957 and now lives in the West Indies.

JAMES AGGREY was born in the Gold Coast in 1875, son of the King's chief counsellor. He was educated at a Mission School and at the age of fourteen he became an ardent Christian. He went to the United States when he was twenty-three in order to study for the Ministry. Whilst he was in America, he studied agriculture and economics and spent much of his time working among the poor people of Carolina. After twenty years' absence he visited the Gold

Coast and in 1921 and 1924 he went to South Africa. Dr. Aggrey was a great orator and a keen worker in the field of race relations. When he died in 1927 he was in America working at Columbia University, New York, for his doctorate of Philosophy.

RAPHAEL ERNEST GRAIL ARMATTOE, poet, anthropologist, historian and physician, was born in 1913 in Denu in the Gold Coast. He was educated in Europe and during the war years he practised as a doctor in Northern Ireland. In 1950 he returned to the Gold Coast and entered politics. He led a delegation to UNO in 1953 and on his way back he became suddenly ill. He died shortly afterwards in Hamburg. Dr. Armattoe published many books of a wide variety, in German, French and English.

MASUPHA BERENG is the grandson of the late Chief Bereng Letsie. He was born at Rothe in Basutoland in 1928 and brought up there. During the war he served in the army in the Middle East and in 1950 he became a switchboard operator at the Royal Naval Armament Depot at Umbogintwini in Natal.

C. ENITAN BROWN, who was born in Ebute Metta near Lagos in 1909, is a railway technician as well as being a writer. He has been head of the school of railway technology in Nigeria.

GLADYS CASELY-HAYFORD, who was the daughter of a well-known lawyer, was brought up in the Gold Coast. When she was fifteen she was sent to Wales to complete her education. She returned to West Africa as a teacher and died there at an early age of blackwater fever. Some of her poems and short stories have been published and broadcast in London.

THOMAS A. CODJOE is an ancient of Accra who stops you after the style of the Ancient Mariner to sell you a political pamphlet, price 1d. In his own person he is an author, type-setter, machine-minder—the press is worked by foot—wholesaler and news-vendor. He does jobbing-printing as well as pamphleteering but is known in Accra as a philosopher who rises superior to the attractions of money. At one time he ran a bi-weekly newspaper, entitled the *Voice of Kushara*, which contained not only the best of Dr. Codjoe's prose but also his poetry. He took an Honours Degree at London University and is a Doctor of Science and Law.

BIRAGO DIOP was born at Dakar in Senegal in 1906. He studied at Saint-Louis at the Lycée Faidherbe. Later he worked as a veterinary surgeon. From an early age he was interested in writing and he spent much of his leisure time in writing poetry and short stories.

DAVID DIOP spent his childhood years partly in France and partly in West Africa. He was born in Bordeaux in 1927. His father came from Senegal and his mother from the Cameroons. He spent much of his early life in hospital and it was there that he acquired a taste for reading. Many of his poems have been published in magazines.

CYPRIAN EKWENSI is a Nigerian writer who has had several books published, including a novel written against the background of Lagos. He lived for several years in England, where he studied pharmacy at London University.

GBEMI is the pen name of a young West African woman living in Ibadan. She was educated in Lagos and in England. On her return to Nigeria, she worked as a schoolmistress for some years. Her stories and articles have been both published and broadcast in her own country.

THE HON. SHEIKH MBARAK ALI HINAWY is a great authority on Swahili literature and history and has done much to bring to light old manuscripts existing in East Africa. He was born in 1896 in East Africa and educated privately and at a school in Mombasa. He served with the King's African Rifles in the First World War and again returned to the army in the Second World War. In 1918 he entered the Civil Service and later he was appointed Liwali (Governor) of Mombasa. He is now Liwali of the Coast, a position he has held since 1942. He is a member of Kenya's Legislative Council and is the personal adviser on Arab Affairs to the Governor.

ISHAK 'the poor man' lived in Ethiopia in the 13th century. He wrote his Ethiopic version of the *Kebra Nagast* (The Glory of Kings), which tells the story of Solomon and the Queen of Sheba at a time when Solomon's line of successors to the Ethiopian throne had been restored.

JOMO KENYATTA was born about fifty years ago in the Kikuyu Reserve. He was educated at a mission school. His first job was as a kitchen boy and he later worked at the water works in Nairobi. He went to London in 1929 to represent the Kikuyu Central Association and gave evidence before the Hilton Young Land Commission. In 1931 he returned to England and stayed for thirteen years and studied at the London School of Economics. On his return to Kenya he was active in land tenure problems.

CAMARA LAYE was working in a factory in Paris when he wrote his first book, *L'Enfant Noir,* the story of his childhood in French Guinea. Later he wrote a novel, *Le Regard du Roi.* He was born in French Guinea in 1924 and he spent the first eighteen years of his life there. On leaving school he was given a scholarship which took him to France to complete his engineering studies.

A. S. LEGODI, who died in 1950, was a Lutheran minister of the Berlin Mission in the Transvaal.

WILLIAM MODISANE was born in Johannesburg in the twenties and brought up in the slums of Sophiatown. His first short story, *The Dignity of Begging,* was published in 1951. For several years he has worked in bookshops in Johannesburg and is now engaged in writing an historical novel.

THOMAS MOFOLO grew up amongst the mountains and pastures of Basutoland, where he was born in 1877. Like most Basuto boys he spent much of his childhood in herding cattle and hunting the wild game that then inhabited the highlands of his country. He went to school in Basutoland, and qualified as a teacher at the Morija Training College. After some years of teaching, he returned to the Morija Book Depot to work as a clerk and proof reader. Later he went to work in Johannesburg, returning to Basutoland in 1912 as labour agent to a group of gold mines. During the years that followed he opened a mill in North Basutoland and later kept a store of his own. It was whilst he was working at Morija that Thomas Mofolo began to write and when he died in 1948 he had published three books, written in his native language of Sotho.

J. SAVERIO NAIGIZIKI was awarded the literature prize of the Brussels Colonial Fair in 1949 for his book *Escapade Ruandaise.* He was born in Ruanda in 1915, and after leaving school he worked as a schoolmaster, a translator, a printer, an assistant chauffeur and an import agent's clerk. He now lives and works in Astrida in Ruanda and has recently published a play.

ABIOSEH D. NICOL is a West African born in Sierre Leone and educated in that country and in Nigeria. In 1943 he went to Europe and took a Degree in Natural Sciences at Cambridge. His poems and short stories have been broadcast by the B.B.C. in London and published in a number of English magazines and newspapers.

KWAME NKRUMAH was born in the Western Province of the Gold

Coast in 1909. He was educated at the Prince of Wales's College at Achimota and graduated from Lincoln University, Pennsylvania, in 1939. After further study in America and in London at the London School of Economics, he returned to the Gold Coast in 1947 to take an active part in politics. He was imprisoned for political agitation in 1950, but was released a year later to form a government. The same year he went to America to receive the honorary degree of Doctor of Laws from Lincoln University. In 1952 he became the first Prime Minister of the Gold Coast and by 1957 his dream of independence for his country was realized.

FRANCIS OBIKA was born at Ogidi in Nigeria. He was educated in Lagos and later qualified at the Yaba School of Pharmacy. He joined the Civil Service, but after five years he resigned in order to practise as an independent pharmacist.

JEAN-JOSEPH RABÉARIVELO was a man of frail stature and a passionate temperament. He was born at Antananarivo in Madagascar in 1901 and committed suicide there thirty-six years later. He was taken away from school at the age of thirteen. He was still a young man when he started taking opium and had become a drug addict when he took his own life. He founded a literary review and had published several books, mostly verse.

JACQUES RABÉMANANJARA started the 'Revue des Jeunes' in Madagascar and has written a play and has published several books of poetry. He was born in Madagascar in 1913 and studied at the Jesuit College at Antananarivo. He entered the Colonial Administration and in 1939 he was sent to France for instruction at the Colonial Ministry. He was in France at the outbreak of war and was unable to return to Madagascar because of the occupation. He spent this time studying for a University Arts degree.

L. D. RADITLADI belongs to the Bamangwato royal family, his grandfather being King Khama's brother. He was educated at mission schools and later at Fort Hare University College. Whilst he was at Fort Hare, his family were banished from Bechuanaland for political reasons by Tschekedi Khama. They were in exile for about fifteen years, but returned to their country after Tschekedi's fall.

FLAVIEN RANAIVO spent all his young days in the country in and around Antananarivo and his writing has been greatly influenced by the country-side of his homeland. He was born in Madagascar in 1914.

OSCAR RIBAS, the blind writer of Angola, was born in Luanda in 1909. He studied there in the College of Salvador Correia, where he was a brilliant scholar. When he was twenty-one years of age he became seriously troubled by the eye disease with which he had been born. He was only sixteen when he began to write and his first story was published in 1927. The first of his books was published in 1948, followed by two others during the next four years. In 1952 his story 'A Praga' ('The Plague') was given the Margaret Wrong Literary Award in London.

RICHARD RIVE was reading Shakespeare, Beecher Stowe and Dickens by the age of twelve, and at that age he would recount stories to other small boys who gathered together on the street corners of District Six, the notorious slum quarter of Cape Town. He was born in the Cape Peninsula in 1931 and went to the University of Cape Town. He has since taken up teaching.

JAMES DAVID RUBADIRI is a schoolmaster in Nyasaland, where he was born in 1930. After graduating from Makerere College, Uganda, he left Africa to study teaching in England. His main ambition as a writer of prose and poetry is to interpret the thoughts and experiences of his own people.

MICHAEL ONTEPETSE MARTINUS SEBONI has had several of his books published and has translated into Tswana Shakespeare's *Henry IV*. He was born in Bechuanaland in 1912 and educated at mission schools and later at Fort Hare University College. He worked as secretary to Chief Kgari Sechele and as a Revenue Clerk in Johannesburg. He took up teaching and became Headmaster of a Bantu High School. Later he was appointed to the staff of Fort Hare.

LÉOPOLD SÉDAR SENGHOR, poet, politician, linguist, was born in 1906 in the heart of Senegal. He studied at Dakar, and at the age of twenty-two he was awarded a scholarship which brought him to Paris. There he became a student at the Lycée Louis-le-Grand and after taking his degree in letters he went on to the Sorbonne. For some years he was a teacher in Tours and in Paris. Then, in 1945 he became the Deputy for Senegal in the French National Assembly and Professor of African Languages and Literature at the École National de la France d'outre-mer. He has published several books of verse and is Political Director of a Dakar newspaper.

DYKE SENTSO was born at Kroonstad in the Orange Free State in

1924. His father was at that time the pastor of the Dutch Reformed Church for Africans. Dyke Sentso was educated and trained as a teacher at the London Missionary Institution of Tigerkloof in the Cape Province. Since leaving, he has taught at a school in Vredefort in the Free State. He is the author of a book in Sotho and of many short stories, some of which have been translated into other languages and published abroad.

M. W. SINAH was born in Sierra Leone in 1923. There he attended Roman Catholic mission schools until 1935. For the next five years he worked as a teacher and then he joined the army from which he was discharged with the rank of sergeant. He is now working for an oil company in Freetown.

DANIEL CANADOCE THEMBA was born in 1924 in South Africa and grew up there in a Coloured community. He was educated in Pretoria and Pietersburg and was awarded the Mendi Scholarship to the University College of Fort Hare. He taught English for several years in Western Native Township, Johannesburg. In 1953 he won *Drum's* short story competition with his story 'Mob Passion' and later he joined the editorial staff of the magazine.

AMOS TUTUOLA was born in 1920 in Abeokuta in West Africa where his father was a cocoa farmer. He was educated near his home and in Lagos. Whilst he was there he used to grind the pepper, wash all the plates, sweep the floor and draw the water for the woman with whom he lodged before he set out for school in the mornings. After his father died in 1938 Amos Tutuola farmed unsuccessfully and later became a blacksmith. He joined the R.A.F. as a coppersmith and after his discharge he carried on with his trade for a few months. Afterwards he joined the Department of Labour in Lagos. Three of his books have been published in London and one of them, *The Palm-Wine Drinkard,* has been translated into four European Languages.

BENEDICT WALLET VILIKAZI is well known for the work he has done to further Bantu literature in South Africa. His own poetry and prose which he wrote in his native language, Zulu, have been published in South Africa. He was appointed to the staff of the Department of Bantu Languages at the University of the Witwatersrand in Johannesburg and became the Senior Language Assistant in the Department, a position which he held at the time of his death in 1947.

ACKNOWLEDGMENTS

WHEN Jim Bailey suggested that I should compile an anthology of writing by Africans from all over Africa, we thought it would probably take no more than three months to complete the necessary research. It took four years.

No anthology of this kind had so far been compiled. Most of the writers were little known. Some of the writing was in French, some in Portuguese and much of it in the many vernacular languages of Africa. Most of it had not yet been translated into English and much of what had been written was still unpublished. Many published works were rare and only to be found in certain Africana libraries.

In order to discover what had been written, I had to consult those who were familiar with the writings of Africans in other languages, and in many cases translations were made into English so that a final selection might be made. Although some of these translations did not eventually find a place in the anthology, they were nevertheless important in the work of choosing material. My thanks and apologies are due to those who gave me such valuable assistance by making these translations.

Since the anthology was not to be a purely academic work, but was intended for the general reader, many good pieces of writing had to be left out because their appeal would be limited. So it is that the student of African writing will inevitably find omissions.

My thanks are due to the many people who made it possible for me to compile this anthology; to those who gave me access to manuscripts and rare editions of Africana books; to those who allowed me to use their libraries; to those who gave so much time to discussing African writing with me and to those who made translations into English, and not least to the many authors who sent me such an abundance of manuscripts. But most of all I am indebted to Jim Bailey for the inception of this book and to my husband for his encouragement and suggestions at all stages of its progress.

My personal thanks are due to: Kenneth Ablack, Adisa Williams and Prudence Smith of the B.B.C. London, for the loan of scripts; Robin Denniston, Faith Press Ltd, London, for his untiring encouragement and criticism; Patrick Duncan, Maseru, for allowing me to use his own Africana library; Jasmine Rose-Innes, Accra, for help with the West African section; M. de Mestral and Miss

Sullivan of the International Committee on Christian Literature for Africa, London, for the loan of books and for the use of their library; Dr. Abioseh D. Nicol for all the time he has so generously given as critic and adviser; Professor C. L. S. Nyembezi, University College, Fort Hare, South Africa, for his valuable assistance in obtaining translations; Miss Ogilvie, Johannesburg Public Library, for her assistance whilst I was working in the Africana section of the library; The Revd. G. Parrinder, University College, Ibadan, for footnotes; Mr. Roberts, The South African Institute of International Affairs, Johannesburg, for permission to work in the Institute's library; Léopold Sédar Senghor, Paris, for footnotes; Mrs. Una Snow for the loan of manuscripts entered for the Margaret Wrong Award; Mrs. B. Wyatt of the International African Institute, London, for her suggestions and for the loan of books.

For their translations into English, my thanks are due to: Dorothy Blair, Johannesburg; Professor D. T. Cole and the late Dr. S. M. Mofokeng, Department of Bantu Languages, University of the Witwatersrand, Johannesburg; G. H. Franz, Native Education Department, Pretoria; L. Hollingsworth and D. M. Stewart, School of Oriental and African Studies, London; Professor Murad Kamel, Cairo University; R. M. Mfeka, Johannesburg; M. D. Mohapeloa, Johannesburg; G. I. Mzamane and L. Mgotsi, University College, Fort Hare, South Africa; Dr. I. D. du Plessis, Cape Town; G. W. Tabor, Johannesburg; Professor Mora de Vasconcelos, University of the Witwatersrand, Johannesburg.

For information and advice, my thanks are due to: Sheikh Yahya Alawi, Information Office, Zanzibar; Dr. Antonio de Andrade, Lisbon; J. C. Baylis, Northern Rhodesia and Nyasaland Joint Publications Bureau; Jean Blackwell, Curator, Schomburg Collection, New York Public Library; Jonathan Curling, Thomas Nelson & Sons Ltd, London; Shaaban Farsi, Education Office, Zanzibar; Sir John Gray, Zanzibar; Marcos Hanna, Légation Impérial d'Ethiopie, Cairo; J. G. S. Harrison, Mombasa; Mrs. Adelaide Casely-Hayford, Sierra Leone; Sheikh Mbarak Ali Hinawy, Mombasa; Claudine Hogg, Longmans Green & Co. Ltd, London; Professor D. D. T. Jabavu, Middledrift, South Africa; Wolf Leslau, Cambridge, Massachusetts; Georges Mabille, Paris Missionary Society, Johannesburg; D. McK. Malcolm, University of Natal; Leo Marquard, Oxford University Press, Cape Town; Methodist Book Depot, Cape Coast, West Africa; J. P. Mohapeloa and Bennett Khaketla, Basutoland; Théodore Monod, Institut Français, d'Afrique Noire, Dakar; L. D. Raditladi, Bechuanaland; Charles Richards, East African Literature Bureau, Nairobi;

C. A. Roy, Shuter & Shooter, Ltd, Pietermaritzburg; Royal African Society, London; The School of Oriental and African Studies, London; Mary Senior, United Society for Christian Literature, London; The Revd. Dr. R. H. W. Shepherd and the Revd. J. J. Jolobe, Lovedale Missionary Institution, South Africa; G. Janson-Smith and W. P. Morrison, Ministry of Education, Sudan; The Revd. Albert Strong, Sudan Interior Mission, Addis Ababa; Henry Swanzy, Accra; Miss E. D. Terry, S.P.C.K., London; Hugh Tracey, African Music Research, Johannesburg; Via Afrika Boekwinkel, Bloemfontein; Stephen Wright, Addis Ababa, and Mr. Zurcher and Mr. Christella of the Morija Sesuto Book Depot, Basutoland.

I have to thank the following persons for their permission to use the items given below:

S. F. Aboderin for 'A Night on the Island'; Peter Abrahams for the extract from his book *Tell Freedom,* published by Faber & Faber Ltd, London; Madame L. E. Armattoe for 'The Lonely Soul' from *Deep Down the Blackman's Mind* by R. E. G. Armattoe.

Masupha Bereng for 'The Prince of the Combined Headquarters'; C. Enitan Brown for 'Marriage Cordiality'; Thomas A. Codjoe for 'O Blue-Sky Duchess.'

Georges A. Deny, Brussels, for 'Escapade in Ruanda' from *Escapade Ruandaise* by J. Saverio Naigiziki.

C.O.D. Ekwensi and Drum Publications for 'Ritual Murder.'

Faber & Faber Ltd, London, for 'My First Wedding Day in the Bush of Ghosts' from *My Life in the Bush of Ghosts* by Amos Tutuola; Fasquelle Éditeurs, Paris, for 'Vérité et Mensonge' from *Les Contes d'Amadou-Koumba* by Birago Diop; G. H. Franz and S. Kgomedi Lekgothoane for 'Song of Praise to the Creator.'

Henry Holt & Co. Inc., New York, for 'Justice' from *The Fire on the Mountain and Other Ethiopian Stories* collected by Harold Courlander and Wolf Leslau and for 'Talk' and 'Anansi's Fishing Expedition' from *The Cow-Tail Switch and Other West African Stories* collected by Harold Courlander and George Herzog.

The International African Institute, London, for 'The Death of Noliwe,' an extract from *Chaka* by Thomas Mofolo, published by the Oxford University Press, London, and for 'Two Bird Songs of the Pokomo Women' which appeared in *Africa.*

E. L. Lasebikan for his translation 'What a Day!'

Macmillan & Co. Ltd, London, for 'The Cunning of Suud' from *Al-Akida and Fort Jesus, Mombasa* by Mbarak Ali Hinawy; William Modisane and Drum Publications for 'The Dignity of Begging.'

Nasionale Pers Beperk, Bloemfontein, for 'Rammone Returns to the Kalahari' from *Rammone wa Kgalagadi* by M. O. M. Seboni;

Thomas Nelson & Sons Ltd, Edinburgh, for the extract from *Ghana* by Kwame Nkrumah; Abioseh D. Nicol and the proprietors of Blackwood's Magazine, Edinburgh, for 'The Devil at Yolahun Bridge'; Nigerian Printing and Publishing Co. Ltd, for 'There's Always a Way Out' by Gbemi; The Northern Sotho Book Depot, Edendale, Transvaal, South Africa, for 'Sotho Boyhood' from *Ruthe wa Moaba* by A. S. Legodi.

Francis Obika for 'The Return of the Soldier'; D. C. Osadebay for his translation 'O Lamb Give me my Salt.'

Sylvia Pankhurst for 'Trousers of Wind,' 'Hymn of Praise,' and her adaptation of 'The Queen of Sheba' from *The Queen of Sheba and her Only Son, Menyelek* by Sir E. A. Wallis Budge, both of which appeared in her *Ethiopia, A Cultural History* published by Sidgwick and Jackson, London; Librairie Plon, Paris, for 'The Stolen Jacket,' an extract from *Le Regard du Roi* by Camara Laye; Presses Universitaires de France, Paris, for the following poems from *Anthologie de la Nouvelle Poésie Nègre et Malgache* compiled by Léopold Sédar Senghor : 'Flûtistes' by Jean-Joseph Rabéarivelo, part of 'Chercheuse d'eau' by Flavien Ranaivo, part of 'Lyre à sept cordes' by Jacques Rabémananjara, 'Congo' by Léopold Sédar Senghor and 'Celui qui a tout perdu' by David Diop.

Oscar Ribas for 'The Angola' from *Ecos da Minha Terra*; Richard Rive for 'The Bench'; James D. Rubadiri for 'Stanley meets Mutesa.'

Secker & Warburg Ltd, London, for 'The Gentlemen of the Jungle' from *Facing Mount Kenya* by Jomo Kenyatta; Dyke Sentso and Drum Publications for 'Under the Blue Gum Trees'; M. W. Sinah for 'The Sergeant who Rejoiced in his Youth'; The S.P.C.K. and the Sheldon Press, London, for 'Much Silence' from *African Aphorisms or Saws from Swahililand* compiled by W. E. Taylor, and for 'The Parable of the Eagle' from *Aggrey Said* compiled by C. Kingsley Williams; Stackbole Co., Harrisburg, Pennsylvania, for 'The Talking Skull' from *African Genesis* by Leo Frobenius and Douglas G. Fox.

D. C. Themba and Drum Publications for 'Mob Passion'; Hugh Tracey for his translations from the Zulu of 'The Body Perishes . . .,' 'Take off your hat . . .' and 'The Committee is at the School . . .' from *Lalela Zulu* and his translation from the Zezuru of 'Keep it Dark' from *Songs from the Kraals of Southern Rhodesia:* both books were published by the African Music Society, Johannesburg.

The Universities' Mission to Central Africa for 'The Story of Liongo' and 'The Monkey who left his Heart in a Tree' (part of 'The Story of the Washerman's Donkey') from *Swahili Tales,* published by Bell & Daldy, London, and for 'The Story of a Bemba Slave Boy' from *Kiungani*, published by George Bell & Sons, London.

West African Review Ltd, London, for 'Shadow of Darkness' by Gladys Casely-Hayford; The Witwatersrand University Press, Johannesburg, for 'Motswasele's Farewell' from *Motswasele II* by L. D. Raditladi and for an extract from 'Umamina' from *Amal' ezulu* by B. W. Vilikazi.

P.R.